Broken Crayons Still Colour:
Understanding Post Traumatic Stress Disorder through Art

First published in Great Britain in 2022 as a self-published work by PTSD UK

PTSD UK is a registered charity SC045995

FIRST EDITION

A catalogue record for this book is available on request from the British Library.

ISBN 978-1-3999-2535-8

PTSD UK is committed to a sustainable future for our business, our supporters and our planet. This
book is made from Forest Stewardship Council ® certified paper (license code: FSC-C022913)

All profits from this book will be donated to PTSD UK - the only charity in the UK dedicated to raising
awareness of Post Traumatic Stress Disorder (both PTSD and Complex PTSD) – the causes, symptoms &
the treatments available – no matter the trauma that caused it. Find out more at PTSDuk.org

THE CONTENTS OF THIS WORK ARE INTENDED TO FURTHER KNOWLEDGE OF
POST TRAUMATIC STRESS DISORDER (BOTH PTSD AND C-PTSD) AND ARE NOT
A SUBSTITUTE FOR MEDICAL ADVICE, NOR SHOULD BE RELIED UPON AS
RECOMMENDING OR PROMOTING A SPECIFIC METHOD, DIAGNOSIS, OR
TREATMENT. THIS BOOK IS SOLD WITH THE UNDERSTANDING THAT THE
NEITHER THE CONTRIBUTORS, AUTHORS NOR PUBLISHER ARE ENGAGED
WITH RENDERING PSYCHOLOGICAL, MEDICAL OR OTHER PROFESSIONAL
SERVICES. IF EXPERT MEDICAL ASSISTANCE IS REQUIRED, THE SERVICES OF A
COMPETENT PROFESSIONAL SHOLD BE SOUGHT.

*This book is dedicated to*

# ALL OF OUR SUPPORTERS

and all the contributing artists featured in this book.

Everything our supporters do helps us on our mission to
support everyone affected by Post Traumatic Stress
Disorder (both PTSD and C-PTSD),
no matter the trauma that caused it.

PLEASE NOTE: This book contains
explicit content and themes

*Broken Crayons Still Colour: Understanding Post Traumatic
Stress Disorder through Art* features artworks from people
affected by PTSD and C-PTSD and so covers some very
difficult and traumatic subjects including (but not limited
to) child abuse, rape, domestic abuse, sexual abuse, drug
addiction, violence, death, suicide and self-harm and
features explicit language and nudity.

> "Art washes away from the soul the dust of everyday life."
>
> -Picasso

Scientific research and anecdotal evidence continues to show that the creation of art has been a successful therapy for PTSD and C-PTSD for many years. Whether it's a poem, sculpture, photograph, painting, illustration, doodle, or haiku, this authentic expression can help people deal with the symptoms of PTSD and C-PTSD, find coping strategies and an internal strength to begin their healing process without having to relive traumatic experiences in a way they don't want to.

The creation of art helps people articulate thoughts, feelings and sensations that are hard (or at times impossible) to put into words: it's an opportunity to 'verbalise' inner emotions without having to talk. It allows people to feel free to experience their emotions at a level that feels right for them at that time, whilst combatting PTSD or C-PTSD symptoms such as avoidance and emotional numbing. The creative self-expression can foster a sense of empowerment, purpose, accomplishment and possibility. It also allows people to share their deep and personal experience of PTSD or C-PTSD in an expressively powerful and liberating way – they are in control of the art they create.

As such, creating an art book seemed like a really insightful and natural way for us to be able to portray what it's like to have PTSD or C-PTSD and to help raise awareness and educate people about the all-encompassing symptoms they can bring to someone's life (and those around them too). We wanted to use these creative expressions to show people they're not alone in their experience with PTSD or C-PTSD and to provide the hope that 'Tomorrow CAN be a New Day'.

The artwork in this book was sent to us as part of a competition. We had entries from all around the UK, from people with PTSD and C-PTSD, people who've been through treatment and recovered, and from friends and family of people with the condition. We judged the entries based on originality, interpretation and impact and we chose 4 top prize winners:

**First Place:** Mel Tebbutt-Bushell's 'Purple Tinged Skin Discolouration'

**Second Place:** Cecilia Bryant's 'I survive'

**Joint Third Place:** Keith Baddam's glasswork and Millie Hardy's 'Unspeakable'

Picking the top prize winners was a really hard task. As the submissions were sent to us, we were overwhelmed with the incredible standard of entries – they were so emotive and powerful. And as a previous PTSD sufferer, I felt such a connection with the people who'd created them. In almost every case, I could *feel* the emotions they were portraying – and oftentimes it was a message of hope, resilience and strength which I found incredibly inspiring. On more than one occasion I cried at the intensely expressive and striking words and images that had been created – and thinking back to my darkest days of PTSD, I so wished that this book had existed then. I really think I would have felt less alone and isolated - I really hope it can bring you some comfort in knowing you truly are not alone in this - and that holding onto hope can be so incredibly powerful.

One of the beautiful things about art and particularly art therapy, is there is no 'right' or 'wrong' way to create it. You create what feels right for you. Much of the artwork you'll see in this book has been created by people with PTSD or C-PTSD who just 'went with it' – they just let the words flow, or the paintbrush take them to where they needed it to. Some people have shared their meaning behind their creation and in other cases, their words or artworks speak clearly for themselves.

In almost all cases, whatever has been created, the people who produced the artwork in this book said it had helped them. For some, it helped them experience their emotions in a more constructive way, others felt a 'release' from the overwhelming and suffocating nature of PTSD or C-PTSD and the symptoms they experience and others felt liberated – they were able to explain what their day-to-day life is like through their art – finally, someone might understand how they feel.

I'd like to personally thank every single person who entered our competition – your

creations have the power to inspire others and provide hope, understanding and empowerment in a new format.

If you're someone with PTSD or C-PTSD who is holding this book, from the bottom of my heart I'm sending you so much love and strength. Our aim is that this book brings you hope, a feeling of resilience or anything else you might need, so feel free to use it as you wish: keep it by your bed for a 3am comfort read, scribble notes in it, highlight the bits that make you feel strong, or put it away in a drawer and bring it out for the days you need it most.

Change and healing IS possible, I'm a living example of that – but if you need our support, PTSD UK is here for you. Please reach out to us and know you're not alone.

Tomorrow CAN be a New Day.

Jacqui Suttie
CEO and Founder of PTSD UK

## Living with Beasts
Lauren Curry
I have C-PTSD

Digital Drawing on ibisPaint

I've always imagined my C-PTSD as a beast that is ready to rip free. The one thing I feel most sufferers want is the ability to get control again. This image is the concept image for a comic idea I'm exploring currently around mental health and acceptance, and how anyone can gain back the control they've felt they've lost.

# Forest
## Graeme Laverty
I have C-PTSD

Acrylics on interior wall

This painting is a huge 7ft x 5 ft mural I have painted in my living room after I taught myself to paint during lockdown. I was diagnosed with C-PTSD after 20 years of not speaking about my struggles.

The next day after the appointment, lockdown started and was put out of work at the same time, I was in a low state of mind and felt lost... the only thing that helped me feel better was spending time in the forest and being creative.

I taught myself wood carving and pyrography and eventually, to colour some of my carvings I bought some cheap paints online and started painting on canvas to help pass the time. I realised that painting was very therapeutic and helps to calm the mind, also by painting nature, forests and water, it helps bring me a sense of peaceful nature without having to leave the house.

This picture took around 1 month to complete with no help from online tutorials, I just started drawing on my wall one day and let my soul guide the brush.

I bought some tester pots and started to create the space I want to be in without having to move house.

I love this painting because it makes the small space I live in feel like it leads into a huge endless forest with high misty mountains. I find myself staring at it and getting lost for hours with a feeling of peace.

## Mind Blown
Linda
A family member has C-PTSD

Oil on canvas

I painted this during lockdown. I'm a novice artist. It represents a beloved family members struggle with long term C-PTSD.

From the dark swells of the sea and the crashing, unforgiving waves to the fear and instability of the ship from which she fears she'll never get off, goes under. The lightning strikes and the clapping thunder suggest the bad days when they completely crash out. There seems no reprieve from it's torment.

There is a faint ray of sunshine high in the sky behind the clouds which represents a glimmer of hope. Because without hope, the heart breaks.

# Veneer
## Pippa Ward
I have PTSD

Falling over me like a veil
No warning signs just blaring alarms
Can't fight it at all
Taking my power and hope
I watch life from the periphery
With the detachment of a professional
Losing count of the times
It's stolen my joy

Cut off from reality
A stranger to myself
Where do I go?
Who should I be?
Who can I trust?
Who can trust me?
Locked in, I'm a prisoner
Of my emotional extremes

If I were brave enough I'd fight
With chemical weapons
A noose or a knife
I'd lock it down tight
But I create a veneer
Posture and pretend
Adjusting my mask

While I take flight again
There's a frequency, a regularity
That it visits me
Here it comes again
Swooping stealth
The hunter and the prey
Rinsed in pain
Continue to hide
While I crumble inside

This poem portrays the effect PTSD has on my day to day life and mental health and how I've had to develop a "veneer" to continue to function within society whilst always at the mercy of my emotional extremes. I wrote it as a free flowing stream of consciousness, like most of my writings. Writing has been my constant companion for as long as I can remember, more powerful than any intervention I've ever received. To purge my soul on the page is to unravel my deepest, darkest corners and try to make sense of my trauma.

## Untitled
Jill Boyd
I have PTSD

Digitally manipulated photography

My photography/art is my way of processing how I feel to enable me to express this outwardly. If I don't, I hold it inwards and have an increase in my anxiety and depression. Without art I would be lost. Diagnosed late in life with autism, creativity has been invaluable.

The image is a 'selfie' edited in a mobile phone app. During a panic attack (due to PTSD) I can't see. I feel like an alien so thought I'd try to portray that in the image. Also, having a voice is so important for self-esteem and self-worth. Art gives me that voice.

# Trauma
## Lauren Ruddock
### I live with C-PTSD

Traumatic memories from days past
Still floating around in the ether
Head a bit smashed
Memories that have already been dealt with
Processed well
I'm no longer under anyone's
Rather poisonous spell
Just every now and then things flicker into my head
No rhyme and no reason
Thought those memories had gone dead
Individuals and their words whizz through my ears
Like a bolt of lightning
Too fast to stay here
Memories don't bother me
They're pretty neutral now
If thoughts wander off for a second
I have to pull them round
So listen here self
It's ok for this to happen
You've fought these things really hard
Take a bow my dear
So excuse me if I'm not triggered
By past action or current words
I'm stronger than my trauma
Processed those memories well.
The past is the past
I'm stronger for what happened
Trauma nearly broke me
But look I'm standing tall.

Poetry has helped me a lot with my mental health, particularly my PTSD and depression. This poem was written in 2020, while I was undergoing EMDR treatment, which was successful, and this helped me to leave things, including the person who caused my trauma and related events, behind me. This helped me to move forward, and I continue to write poetry as I enjoy both writing and performing it, and it helps me express emotions and thoughts that sometimes I don't feel that I can talk about but I can write about. When I'm writing I can physically feel the weight of the emotions lifting from me.

**Breathe**
**Anonymous**
I have PTSD

A ghostly breeze across my back
A subtle reminder of days gone past
A trauma of memories
Demons and men
A distant memory of who I was then

I embrace the warmth
Upon my shoulders
And breathe in deeply

The air and light
It's just that simple

I own this body
And mind
And soul
Not the past
Or the ghosts and the ghouls

I was in an abusive relationship and as a consequence I live with PTSD. I have been lucky enough to receive excellent counselling that has helped me to deal with symptoms of PTSD but there are days when something simple can remind me of the fear and trauma that I suffered at the hands of my abuser. On one particular day I had woken from a night terror and found myself crying, in a sweat and shaken. As I lay in bed the sun shone in through my window and the warmth embraced me and comforted me. I wrote this poem to remind myself to breathe, be still and be present. I am safe.

## The transformation in C-PTSD: Soothing the old self

Caren Wright

I have C-PTSD

Sketch pencils and paper

I sketched this piece of artwork to show the difficulty of transformation during C-PTSD. You flower and blossom into a new you, whilst still carrying the pain and memories of the past.

I disassociated a lot during my healing process, and found it hard to recognise myself... eventually I realised that I was never going to be the same... I was becoming a better version of my former self, but I had to comfort and heal the former version of myself.

This sketch shows the trapped, darker past... being nurtured by the new progressive self showing growth and transformation. I still have a long way to go yet, but this image reminds me to be kind to myself.

## No Way Out
## Stuart Hadfield

Photography

After many years of active addiction, which I believe was a traumatic experience, I made a decision to ask for help and change my life for the better.

One of the things that has helped me is my photography, and this image reminds me of trauma, PTSD, and not being able to see a way out.

## I can do it.....
Lisa Hoddinott

Pencil on paper

It was the first time I'd really been able to sit and draw something since my trauma. This was in my head so I put it on paper. I kind of think it speaks for itself without having to say anything.

# Purple Tinged Skin Discolouration
## Mel Tebbutt-Bushell
I have C-PTSD

It's painful to touch, tender to feel,
The slightest of things makes your mind reel
Cartwheels and somersaults, Salchows and spins,
Dizzying and distracting, but only now it begins...

A memory, a taste, a smell out of place,
You're trapped out of now and cannot escape,
Locked in a cinema of reruns that you hate,
Strapped into the chair, you just have to wait.

No popcorn, no drink, no overpriced food,
Just revisiting the feelings that lower your mood,
Over and over the pain comes again,
Public embarrassment or the loss of a friend.

No horror required, but sometimes it helps
The dealer is dealing and now you've been dealt,
You don't feel like playing, but it's already begun,
The ante is suffering and the pot is glum.

With the movie still playing, and the cards in your hand,
You realise your life is not going as planned,
The next film is starting, it must be getting late,
You look at your cards - they're Aces and Eights.

It's getting too much, you want it to stop,
I don't want to see this one, you're handed the pot,
Weighed down by your winnings, you have not a choice,
Synapses are firing, overloading your voice.

You know what is coming, so why are you so shy?
Your body starts shaking, you stifle a cry,
Mind in full turmoil, your eyes start to glisten,
You open your heart, but no one will listen.

Words are like weapons when wielded by savages,
Committed to memory and all of time's ravages,
Carving your soul with wounds festering and deep,
You opened your heart, now the scars start to weep.

You're flirting with madness, becoming a loon,
Dancing with echoes to your memory's tune,
All of your senses burning with such clarity,
With each perfect recall, you're forgetting your sanity.

Waltzing in circles around the ballroom of your mind,
In this great place even love you won't find,
Nor the comfort of the sweetest of dalliances,
Just the heartbreak and loss of broken alliances.

A constant replay of things that have ended,
And futile attempts of your sacrifices to mend it,
For a moment you see it, the face of your enemy,
It's blank and uncaring and it fills you with envy.

You're pushed through a door marked with regrets,
You've been here before, it's as good as it gets,
A cellar of whining, gets worse with age,
You're a mining canary, in your guilded cage.

A song for release, beautiful to the ear,
Keeps you enslaved to your greatest of fears,
The harder that you struggle to break free,
The closer you become to more misery.

The stronger your mind, the greater the pain,
Shovelling the coal for your thought train,
Out of control, yet on only one track,
It has to go further, before you can get back.

Exhausted and broken, stretched wafer thin,
You finally return to where you came in,
If only your mind could show trauma like skin,
People could see it, discoloured with a purple tinge...

I wanted to put into words how it feels to have a PTSD attack. I wanted to give hope to others and show how sufferers are alone in their mind, but not in their suffering. More than all this, I wanted to raise awareness through imagery so those who do not suffer from PTSD could start to empathise with us. Once I started it, my creative process did this with no rewrites, it was a very cathartic process.

# Vines
## Jemma Furnival

Stress constricts me,
Like vines, tight like rope.
Squeezing and suffocating,
What's left of any hope.

It tightens around me,
And it won't be untied,
It twists and pulls me,
Crushing my insides.

It crunches my neck,
While contorting my spine,
The whole while I focus,
On trying to act fine.

## Untitled
Tanya Robertson

Sometimes PTSD feels like I'm climbing mountains and getting nowhere and sometimes I see how far I've come and how I have gained a better perspective of the world in spite of it!

I expected painting my feelings to look black, gory and depressing but instead I think my paintings show that I see and feel a lot and that expressing myself honestly can be beautiful in its own way!

# The Mito Warrior
## Anna Bateman
I have C-PTSD

Her armour was forged
from the fiery
vexations of life
It's breastplate infused
with resilience, rawness
and undeniable
strength
With her companions -
Empathy, Perseverance
and Positivity
She wielded the
sword named
"Let them come"
&
She conquered
Mind's chaos
with confidence,
courage and clarity

This poem was written during my stay in neurological rehabilitation after my fight in intensive care from multiple organ failure and sepsis. I was diagnosed with Mitochondria and to this day I am still a mystery as my type is extremely rare. I found myself again after though, and despite each day being a whirlwind of emotions and physical struggle, I still managed to find the motivation and determination to fight through and get my strength back.

Complex PTSD is a hard battle, but there are definite perks to being stubborn, and when you come out the other side of something you never thought you would ever see, you then realise exactly how much worth it all was. Then the road to inner peace starts.

# Hello PTSD my old friend

Anita Keryell
I have PTSD

Hello PTSD, my old friend.

I have grown to know you well over the years. Many would find it strange this co-dependent relationship you and I share. But I have long since realised that compassion for you is the key.

In the beginning, I am not ashamed to admit that I hated you for all that you stood for, the hurt, the pain and fear. I didn't want to get to know you. I only wanted to push you as far away from me as I could. I stuck my fingers in my ears and refused to listen to your anguished cries. So those cries got louder and more urgent. They tore away at my soul, splintering each horrific memory you wanted to share with me into minuscule shards. Each one burrowed deep into my flesh so that even moving now would remind me of that pain. Every day, you would lie in wait, leaping out to catch me, grabbing my hand roughly and dragging me away to show me yet another dark place. I began looking around each corner for you even when you weren't there. I was terrified of that moment when you would squeeze my heart painfully and put your sweaty hand across my face so I could no longer catch my breath. In the small hours of the night, I would sob quietly into my perpetually soggy pillow. My eyes wide open, listening as you whisper fear, shame and regret to me in the dead of night.

Then one day, it just happened. I took my fingers out of my ears and began to listen to what you had to say. No longer did I have to be dragged with you.

I willingly trotted bravely along beside you. Instead of screaming at each other, we began to talk, and I learned how scared you were for me. How eager you were to protect me and the heavy burden of knowing you never could. It was then I called you a friend. I put my arms around you and listened while you cried. Held your hand tight and taught you how to believe and trust again.

We have grown a lot, don't you think old PTSD and me. Still, you warn me gently of dangers I do not see. But we negotiate now. I don't need to go to the dark place to see anymore. You tell me why it reminds you of the bad times. Then I explain why it is not the same, and together now we vow to give it a try.

We work as partners to keep me safe, my good old friend PTSD and me.

*Writing is how I get what is in my head out into the world. I find it helps not only me but those around me too. It helps me to face my fears and to work out solutions to my problems. Sometimes by writing fiction I can literally rewrite the endings to my bad experiences.*

## "Not my Circus..."
## Victoria McDonald
I have C-PTSD

Mixed media collage on heavyweight art paper

I was diagnosed with Complex PTSD in late 2020 due to an overwhelming mix of personal and professional events.

I underwent trauma therapy & EMDR at the start of this year.

When I started to feel a bit better and more positive, I decided to create a series of mixed media collages that I felt represented my personal journey, that allowed me to both reflect and look forward.

The process allowed me to lose myself in creativity and gave me a welcome distraction and an outlet to express what I found words just could not. I feel this was and is an important, integral part of my therapy.

For once, I was engaging in something that allowed me to focus solely on myself.

This piece, entitled "NOT MY CIRCUS..." is based on the saying I like of "Not my circus, not my monkeys" and represents me finally realising the importance and need to remove myself from negative situations and people that aren't serving or helping me, and to prioritise my own self care and recovery, which I used to think was selfish, but I now realise is absolutely necessary.

## Untitled
## Lynsey Bessent
I have C-PTSD


The seed of anxiety is planted within
Its fed and watered by others
and quickly grows out of control
Into a huge thick solid oak tree
So wide and tall and strong
Its like its been there decades
Its strength like a heard of elephants stampeding
No one else is aware of it
Even though it has taken over my entire body
No one can see it
No one can feel it
No one knows it is there
But I do
I feel it growing within me
Feel it invade my every space
I feel it trapping me
Like I am frozen to the spot
Yet my mind is running round and round in circles
Like a headless chicken
Desperately seeking a way out
An answer
A way to soothe the fear and panic that consumes me
Longing for someone to understand
Knowing I am different
Knowing I won't sleep tonight
As the fear squeezes me by the throat
Knowing it will overwhelm me
And the memories will crash in
I cannot stem the tears
My eyes red and puffy
My nose sore and blocked
My heart hurting more than I could ever say
You keep landing more emotional blows
Swat my experience and feelings away like an annoying fly
To you its because I've not grown up
You just do not understand
I want so much to tame this
To stop it in its tracks
I've spent years learning about it

Learning about myself
Trying to understand
You say you want me to talk to you
But when I do you take it personally
I don't know how to explain
I haven't got the words
I know that it is not my fault
That I have C-PTSD
But if only I knew how to stop the seed planting
Then it wouldn't be able to grow
I will always keep on fighting
No matter how hard it feels
Because I know there can be something better
But for now I have to sit with my feelings
Let the flames of pain die down
And hope tomorrow's a better day
I have to keep striving
Keep hoping and believing
That I can control this
Before it breaks me
You don't know my story
You don't feel my pain
So please don't make assumptions
Please don't break my heart
Just support me when I need it
And walk beside me in my pain
Together we can do this
Then I can be free.

This is extremely important to me as due to my selective mutism and C-PTSD my writing is probably my only means of confident self expression and the way I am most likely to be able to explain my feelings.

## Ground and Grow
Jodie Wright
I have C-PTSD

Pencil colour on paper

I was diagnosed with Complex PTSD 8 years ago. I joined an art therapy group 4 years ago and since then art has been a very good tool to help with distraction. This drawing is made up of simple 'doodles'. Doodling helps to keep me grounded when my PTSD is particularly bad. It is in the shape of a tree to represent growth. The darkness of the trunk represents the dark side of PTSD symptoms and the colourful bloom represents that no matter what and no matter how long it takes, things can get brighter as you grow through your recovery journey.

## Free the Mind
Lozinky
I have PTSD

The artwork I have created is a picture taken of me sitting by a lighthouse trying to free my mind. The picture is edited to create a double vision version to explain how someone like myself with PTSD can have a vision of now and a vision of then... flashbacks for example or a puzzled head.

The caption is a meaning of wishing I had a choice that I'd be much more free and happier.

## The Guardians
Ian Hodgson
I have C-PTSD

Having severe and complex PTSD, getting lost in the detail of a drawing takes me away from the hypervigilence, anxiety, lack of self belief and low self-esteem. Allowing me, for a few hours to be alone from these nightmares. I am single, live alone, I do have a dog. I guess the title I have given this, I suppose is an indication of my hoping that I can find someone to help me with this illness and the days when it is bad. To guard me.

The drawing was donated to the charity, 2 Wish, who provide bereavement support to families who have lost a child/ young person.

## Well-Known Stranger
Rachel G

Acrylic on canvas

My painting is called 'The Well-Known Stranger' and is acrylic on canvas. Going through therapy I found painting as a real outlet for my emotions when I struggled to talk about things I had been through.

The idea of 'The Well-Known Stranger' is this paradox of knowing exactly what PTSD and poor mental health is, how it feels, how horrible it is and knowing it so so well; compare to when it hits, it feels like a complete stranger that floors me and makes me feel unsafe. It hits so hard and can feel incredibly debilitating. It's like I don't know it at all and I have no idea how to handle it or to feel safe again.

So, when having a wobble, I pick up my paint brush and this is one of the paintings that has come out. Purely from emotion and frustration.

# C-PTSD poem on my very own experience
## Daniella Carter
I have C-PTSD

1: CPTSD is like a pain that never leaves,
It curls around me, taking all my control.
Sometimes it shakes me,
Whilst it brakes and crushes my soul.

2: When it becomes night it starts to fall,
When I am curled up in a ball,
And feel like nothing can help me at all.

3: Horrific nightmares waking me up,
Body sweats, shaking and heart rate going up.
Traumatic memories evocating me and my soul.
Please PTSD, go away and leave me alone!

4: The graphic memories come travelling back,
In the dark hours of the night
Leaving me scared, oh no not another attack....
Will there ever be light?

5: Always the same never-ending dream,
Every time I wake up about to scream.
I have tried to overcome it since childhood,
But comes back and burns me like a piece of wood.

6: The memories of the events take me to those places,
Then my body starts to rise and forgets the faces. (dissociate)
Always haunting,
It is so sooo exhausting.

7: All the bad events broke my mind,
I myself am blind.
Blind of life
Each night I wish my mind had a knife. (A knife to cut out the memories)

8: When remembering, it has more power,
Feeling trapped in a sour tower.
My mind rejects, I don't just remember, I feel the event.
And its complete torment.

9: After the trauma,
my heart went hard like a rock,
I was threatened and tortured,
And was not allowed to talk.

10: I began hating as I was hurt,
From that event I am on alert.
My brain automatically disconnects,
All because of the traumas effect.

11: I never know how I am still alive today,
I fight every hour of the day.
I will climb the tallest mountain and touch the sky,
And fight away the lies.

12: I tell my story to help awareness,
And prevent unfairness.
I will continue to rise,
Until this pain finally dies.

I wrote this poem based on how my experience with PTSD and how I have and still do suffer from nightmares and flashbacks but it will never defeat me. Putting my thoughts into art is the most powerful way and art is really effective for my PTSD.

## Untitled
**Tracey Griffin**
I have PTSD

I created this piece of art in relation to my PTSD Therapy journey. I find art to be hugely beneficial in managing intrusive thoughts and feelings and physical memory and a way to control actually being in relived memories and triggers.

Enduring many years of mental health illness, art has helped me to express thoughts and feelings and emotions I have not been able to understand or talk about with anyone.

I have lived always with hope to recover and achieve things I never thought possible and art has become part of my everyday coping strategies to help me understand and manage my symptoms.

Art has become a huge part of my healing journey and I have grown through its benefits and I am still growing and hope to continue to grow and evolve through expressing my inner world this way.

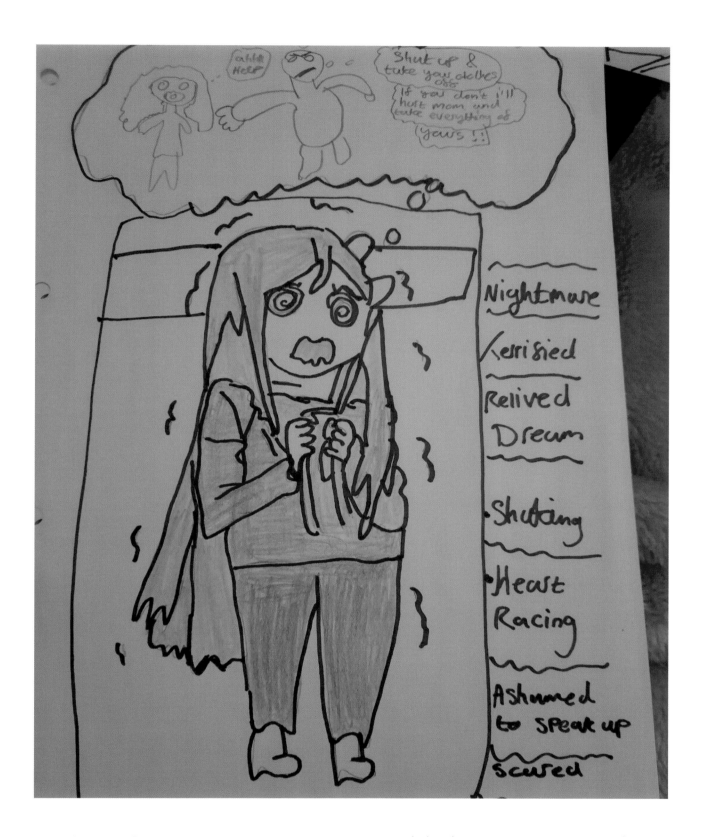

**Waking up in Terror**
Daniella Carter
I have C-PTSD

Pencil and sharpie on paper

I created this because sometimes my dreams crush my soul because I think it's real - like many others with PTSD will do too.

# Untitled

**Ray Moxon**
I have PTSD

I went to the Doctor. They put me on pills.
I went to the Psychiatrist we talked of my ills.
I went to a charity they turned me away.
The Psychologist discharged me 'you're beyond help' she did say.
At the end of my tether to a wood I did go.
Over a branch the rope I did throw.
At the very last moment I changed my plan.
I didn't want to be found, by child or a man.
Suicide leaves a lasting impact in place.
Memories of smells, the look on the face.
So if you're desperate and losing all hope.
Please don't reach for the pills or the rope.
Reach out and speak to a friend or a lover.
Maybe a sister, your Mum or your brother.
Suicides not painless it's simply not true.
The world needs everyone.

Especially you.

I've had first hand dealings with victims of suicide and attempted suicide as well as people who were desperately mentally ill in my role as a specialist search dog handler, and so as I'm ex-emergency services my name is a Nom de Plume to keep my real identity confidential.. My experiences contributed to my PTSD and one of my coping mechanisms is to write poems. This one details my experiences of being in the NHS mental health system.

## Untitled
Debbie Smith

This is my collage artwork on fragmented identity, which I used my own face to create around it.

It signifies that not only does PTSD make you suffer, but you don't remember the true person you used to be. Art therapy is a great way to release a build up of pressure and release your feelings onto paper/canvas and use different mediums.

I get itchy feet to pick up a pen/pencil and create something, then using a mixture of mediums. A lot of people get either lost in music or lost in art.

## Creatures
## Christina D'Ascendis
I have C-PTSD

Soft Pastels

This was another drawing done in the early hours in soft pastel, when my symptoms were very bad and I was going days without sleeping.

I was playing my favourite video game at the time for distraction, which involves zombies and creatures stalking the main characters. The game and the feeling of vulnerability and terror resonated with my own feelings of being constantly stalked by my own traumas and fighting for my own survival, so I started working on this piece, which signifies the terror and exhaustion I was feeling, portrayed through the main character and one of the iconic monsters from the game.

Art helps me tremendously as I can express things I cannot verbalise. It's a visual experience but also a tactile one - I love working with soft pastels and feeling the soft pigment on my fingertips.

# My own life sentence
## Vicky

Three years ago my life was the best
Then as I was getting my head down for a rest
In that split second it changed for the worse
Has someone casted a curse.

My son had been on a night out
Unfortunately he bumped into some louts
Who attacked him leading to his death
I never knew that day he'd take his last breath

From seeing him on that slab
The wound what killed him was a stab
I've never been the same
PTSD is now in my name

The flashbacks, the nightmares is part of my life you know
Why did my son have to go
The depression and anxiety, the sleep deprivation
How did I end up in this situation?

My Son was taken away on a night out, tragically. He was in the wrong place at the wrong time. Attacked by a man who stabbed him in the neck, resulting in him loosing his life. A big part of me died that day. I don't even recognise myself any more.

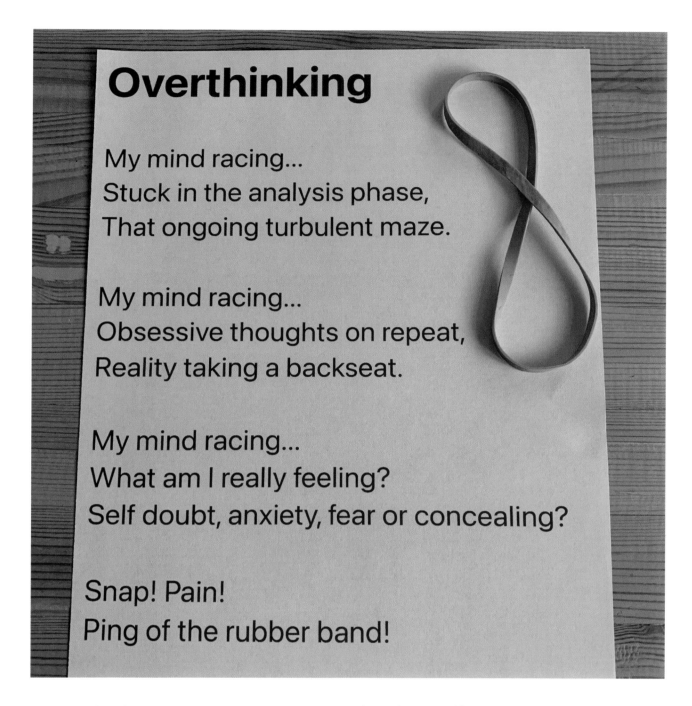

# Overthinking

My mind racing...
Stuck in the analysis phase,
That ongoing turbulent maze.

My mind racing...
Obsessive thoughts on repeat,
Reality taking a backseat.

My mind racing...
What am I really feeling?
Self doubt, anxiety, fear or concealing?

Snap! Pain!
Ping of the rubber band!

**Overthinking**
Claire Hellier

I describe myself as 'One Woman, a thousand thoughts'. Mother, Fiancée, Vocational Trainer and Survivor of Domestic Abuse. I have found old fashioned pen and paper to be my friend during difficult times. I can scribble thoughts, feelings without a structured format I can think critically and process information this way.

My poem, Overthinking. shares my aversion therapy trick when I'm overthinking by using the snap of a rubber band. Simple poem, simple text, simple rubber band, simple technique.

# Untitled
## Molly Kent
I have C-PTSD

Rug Tufting (Mixed fibre, polyester fabric and latex glue)

Untitled is part of Kent's newest series 'Dream Weaving,' a series which picks up themes and ideas from her main body of work to date 'Doubt in the Digital Age,' but represents these themes in a more honest fashion.

'Dream Weaving' deep dives into feelings of loss, anxiety, and trauma which stems from the artist's experiences with C-PTSD, and many of the images created in this series were seen by the artist as strange anxiety fuelled dreams/nightmares.

This work examines the idea of translating the artist's mental state to that of a pictorial narrative. The flames represent her state of being cradled, but somewhat out of control with reference to digital worlds that often have more negative than positive effects on the artist. The artist's hands and arms feature in neon-like depiction, incomplete and un-whole, her identity masked, a shell of herself. How long until the flames grow too large to contain?

## Sea of Emotion
### Amanda Carroll
I have C-PTSD

Acrylic paint and my fingers

I painted this with acrylics when I was overwhelmed with terror, just getting it down on paper calmed me a little. I mainly used my fingers, just threw it on fast, as I painted I realised I was so angry too, angry at what had happened. Angry that they got away with it and I'm left like this struggling day to day. So I painted the sky red to symbolise the anger I feel.

When I'm like this I feel so small, scared, vulnerable. The small boat is me on what feels like a vast sea, on my own with no one that can help. The big wave is the terror about to swallow me whole as the terror overwhelms me.

As I finished the painting I realised I'd painted a small gap where I could sail through and leave the terror 'monster' behind.

## Night time Turmoil and The many faces of Sadness
Claire McMahon

Oil Painting

This is Night time Turmoil and The many faces of Sadness, hypervigilance, numbness, anger then the peacefulness that is sometimes found in moments and the fresh hope for every new day.

I enjoy painting and this helps me feel calm and in the moment.

# The Unseen Child
## Lorna Tait

PTSD and my life
9 years old sitting in the headteachers office
Well I'm afraid we have had to call you in as Lorna has been fighting again!
But why? my mother looked at me as if to say
"let the world swallow us up now"
I looked at my Mother & shrugged my shoulders
So once again I was labelled as
"the naughty child"
But what did I do wrong I thought?
Why do adults think they know everything but yet none of them has noticed me the little me the one who was hurting so deeply

PTSD in my teens
I was still trying to figure myself out as I stared down at 4 empty bottles of prescription pills on my bedroom floor and laying there beside them was 3 bottles of vodka staring back at me begging for my love
Later a trip to A&E and the realisation that self-medicating Is not working anymore
and the shame, oh the shame and how heavy it is to carry
I am alone and you are my only friend PTSD

PTSD in my 30s
Well hello my old friend, you've returned again!
I wonder what you have in store for me this time
You see I'm comfortably numb now
"Oh, so I thought"
PTSD why do you always return with that bittersweet knowledge, the knowledge of an event I want to ignore

PTSD in my 40s
Well done PTSD you've finally caught back up with me
My mind and body are no longer one, you've got a tight hold on me now you see, a hold I have been trying to battle for so long
Stop repeating that song
Play it once more
Shhh what was that sound?

Please don't shout
Who's at the door?
Don't let the darkness in
Turn the light on
No turn it off
Leave me alone
No please don't go
Stay with me when I sleep
No leave me in peace

PTSD
I tried to ignore you
I thought you were not real
I coped all these years before
"Or so I believed"
I have figured I can no longer fight you
But instead I have to understand you
To be more aware of your triggers
"or should I say mine"
I don't think I will ever be your friend PTSD
"But now I know you so well"
And it's from this knowing
That I understood I will once again survive YOU my old friend.

I guess I always thought it was me, I am PTSD
But I am not, you are separate to me,
Although you like to walk by my side and sometimes lead me
I am & always will be me
Little Lorna

This is a piece of writing that has been written straight from my soul & heart, I am currently undergoing specialist trauma counselling and it has taken me 34 years to finally get to this point of understanding myself and all that I am. Writing has helped me over the years as I can not always make sense of my thoughts and feelings, however when I write I feel like I have control over PTSD instead of PTSD having control over me. I'm still on my journey and I'm still finding new roads to recovery but I am the little me and the adult me all rolled into one just trying to figure it all out.

## Blue Window
Mina
I have PTSD

Digitally manipulated photography

PTSD affects me greatest in the mornings. I often wake early and struggle to shake the feelings and emotions that come along with an intense emotional and argumentative experience, yet these feelings originate from a situation that I am not currently experiencing, those trauma's lingering within me and being difficult to shake off. I find that focusing my mind on producing digital art helps me contextualise and place these feelings better within my mind, and enables me to get on with my day better when an attack occurs.

After a traumatic period in my life I ended up living in a hostel. There I had to find my feet and my strength again, which I did with the help of my friend (pictured in the piece).

During our stay together at the hostel we became lifelong friends, helping each other to grow from our experiences and find happiness again both individually and in friendship.

I took a series of photos of her staring from the window in her room with her permission. She would spend long hours here, day dreaming of the possibilities the future might hold. I would do the same from my window.

I made this piece from those photographs, in an attempt to show that although she was blue in this period, and felt trapped by her surroundings, that she found a way to dream and hope about the future through that window she would sit in. My experience paralleled hers, much like our adjoining rooms.

Today we have both moved on from the hostel, and are regaining our lives day by day. I believe hope and believing in each other carried us through that time.

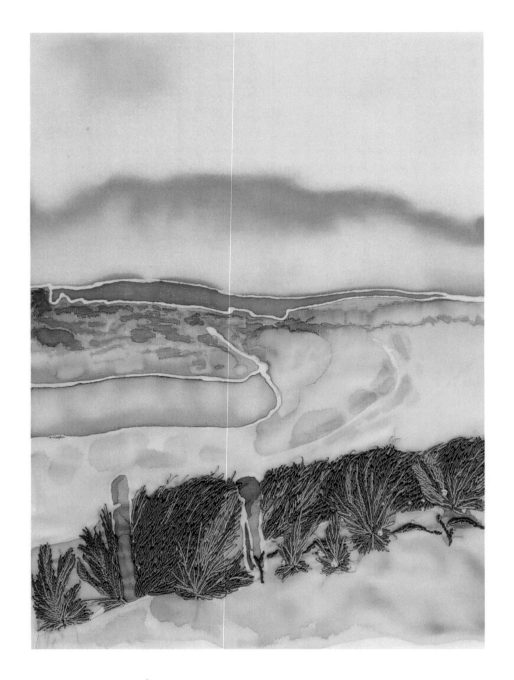

"We all need a safe place to retreat to, a place to take a deep
breath and remind ourselves "We are OK! We can do this!"
Whether that is a real place or a place in our minds matters little.
Take your safe place with you. Practice going there often."

## A Safe Place
Rachel Nicholls
I have C-PTSD

Painting on silk with embroidered detail

I started to paint images in silk which were inspired by my own journey through trying to recover from Complex PTSD and Anorexia with the hope they may bring hope and encouragement to others who were also struggling. This piece was created using silk painting and embroidery and depicts my own safe place.

## Re:purpose:d
Amanda Burridge
I have PTSD

I transform everyday objects into something different. So the picture is of an easter egg tin from a posh chocolate company. My PTSD is both my muse and my nightmare.

I use it to inspire individual pieces where, like through PTSD, we individually become something transformed, reshaped and repurposed in the world. Sometimes we are unrecognisable from our former selves. But we never the less have a place in life.

# Mind in the Sand
## Vicky
My husband has PTSD

Don't tell me to man up or that you understand,
Because I lost my husband somewhere in the desert sand,
His body is at home but his mind is still out there,
Replaying it every night tell me how that's fair,
A man of 19 that saw his life flash before his eyes,
Now he lives with nightmares hearing comrades cries,
Don't tell me it's OK or that you understand,
That he flinches everytime when I try to hold his hand,
He lost his friend in battle and he lost his mind at war,
Now he's struggling just to find a life worth living for,
To the army he's just a number but that number is my one,
Slowly watching him dissappear and soon he will be gone,
My husband wasn't a casualty he still has every limb,
The thing that is killing him so slowly is his demons hid within
So how can I explain what I'm stressing for,
When he's running late or just walked out the door,
Will it be today his name is added to a list,
Another forgotten soldier that the government have missed,
Greeted from war with a country filled with pride,
But then left alone with the demons to hide,
Once a strong hero, now lost in civvy street,
Struggling to find a way to get back on their feet,
Some turn to drugs others to drink,
Just to block out the terrors that they think,
The brotherhood is lost and the calls soon end,
Another distant memory another faded friend,
No support for a hero with nowhere else to turn,
Another life gone, when will our army learn?

I created this poem in honour and awareness of my husband who suffers from PTSD from two tours of Afghanistan, it shows a side to Combat PTSD very rarely seen, the perspective of a loved one and the secondary pain it causes. I have found his PTSD doesn't just affect him but our whole family and home, something none of us were prepared for.

## Strength and Balance
Davy Coyle
I have C-PTSD

Pyrography on wood

I created this piece by medium of pyrography. I started this therapy as a means to suppress the trauma endured as a child and teenager.

It's a Celtic strength and balance symbol. It signifies the need for balance in your life and how to be strong when life proves difficult. It has helped me greatly as I can drift away and let the negativity dissipate whilst doing my art work.

**PTSD**
## Carol Gillon
## I have PTSD

Here we go again,
I just wish I could forget.
My heartbeat is racing,
and I'm beginning to sweat.

The memories replay in my head,
as the fear seems everywhere.
the memories forever haunt me,
it's as if I'm still right there.

I'm caught up in the moment,
going over and over the facts.
PTSD is draining,
it's got me tired to the max.

I can't eat and can't sleep,
as my brain just won't rest.
As PTSD,
has truly put me to the test.

I suffer from PTSD due to trauma. This explains how it makes me feel. Every day its like fighting a never ending battle. Someone caused me the trauma, physically, mentally and emotionally, but now I'm left to fight the war that rages within.

## Fear of Happiness
Rebecca Clinton

Acrylics on a ¾ inch thick piece of wood

My life has been one major incident after another, so much so that whenever I let myself be happy again, something would happen and I would come crashing back down. So I became conditioned to not being happy, not allowing myself to let go and fearing what would happen if I let my guard down again to be happy.

I still do not know how to be happy… I am assured it will come back in time. This painting shows my emotion in its raw form and helped me to identify my fear. The painting represents shrinking back from being happy as I am afraid to go there.

Painted in acrylics on a ¾ inch thick piece of wood. No pre-planning – Using only my hands to manipulate the paint, I let my emotions lead the colours and movements that created this piece.

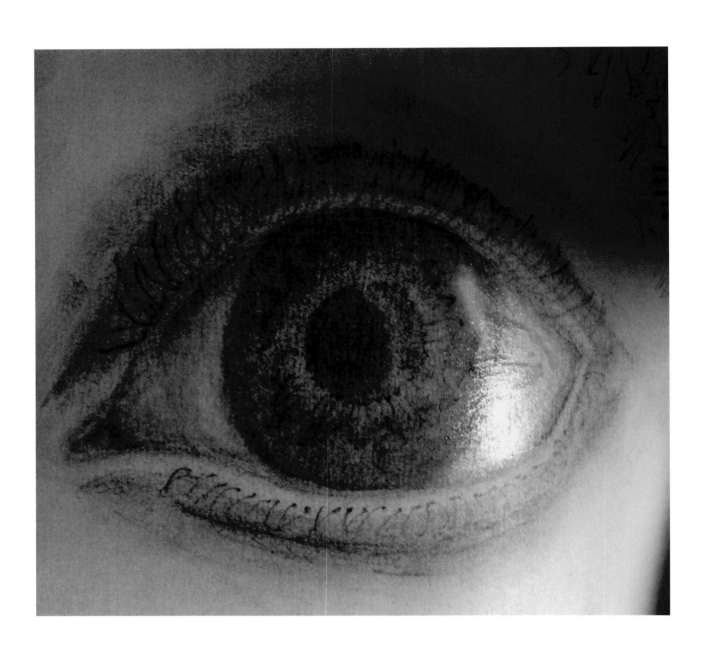

# Look Me In The Eye
## Martin Brighty
I have C-PTSD

Pencil graphite, coloured pencils and acrylic gloss varnish to give a sheen and create reflection of light

I used to love drawing before my incident, but gave up afterwards, I think I felt liking art reflected that I wasn't strong and that's why I was attacked, I was 14 at the time.

I was eventually diagnosed in 2016 with PTSD, and in 2018 apart from doodles I decided to draw a bit more as my young daughter was getting into drawing…. we created pictures together…called the adventures of 'Piggly Oddtrotter and Barnbaby Bear'… which she coloured in.

I surprised myself, that I was patient enough and could still draw and progressed on and am now currently illustrating my own PC game.

I've found art so helpful and a bit frustrating at the same time, but in a good way. I can lose myself for many hours, just relaxing, it doesn't have to be brilliant, it just has to help aid calmness, forgetting my anxieties for a bit, being creative is an experience and I wish that I hadn't punished myself all those years ago by stopping.

My picture here… someone commented that the eyes I draw in my pictures always seemed a bit real, I was told that it's most probably because I have PTSD, but I don't know…. to me eyes are the window to a soul, they reflect everything about the person, happiness, sadness, indifference, fear and love.

# Breaking free from PTSD

Chloe Hunt
I had PTSD and have recovered
through treatment in the form of CBT
(Cognitive Behavioural Therapy)


Traumatic memories repeated over and over in my head,
It filled me with dread.
It was like my mind was being hijacked,
Each flashback took me back,
I felt trapped in the nightmare of my past,
All because I kept my emotions masked.
Years after the trauma PTSD was triggered,
It was like my mind couldn't configure.
Flashbacks and nightmares consumed me,
I felt like I couldn't break free,
It was like reliving the trauma all over again,
I felt like I was going insane,
And felt a sense of shame.
It felt so real,
It was a massive deal,
I seen it as a sign of weakness,
I could just view bleakness.
My high standards sent me backwards,
I felt totally out of control,
It had a massive emotional and physical toll.

I hid the struggle for years,
Bottled up emotions mainly anxiety and fear.
I tried to live life to the full and have cheer,
But my mind was far from clear.
I fooled myself into thinking I was doing well,
It was like I had put myself under a spell,
I felt like I shouldn't dwell on what happened,
I found life post cancer harder than I imagined.
I felt pressure to carry on,
But the old me was gone.

When I finally let my true feelings break free,
The more clearly I could see.
That it is ok to feel different emotions,
And I shouldn't be self loathing.

I am successful,
I am respectful,
I am confident,
I am resilient,
I am strong,
I do belong,
I am loving,
I am giving,
I am compassionate,
I am adequate,
I am funny,
And my personality is sunny.

By retraining my mind,
And being kind,
I now have a different perspective,
I can now be more reflective.
I can think about my past horror, without terror.
Although it was unbelievably hard,
I eventually let down my guard.
Now I have started to put the pieces of my past together,
I now feel light as a feather.
I feel relieved,
I feel better than I could have ever believed.
I have reclaimed my usual spark,
I feel like I am no longer in the dark.
I can now look ahead and dream,
I am now going upstream.
With my determination I wont give in,
I will always win,
Don't mess with me,
I will always break free.

My poem was written as a way to express myself. I was very reluctant to write to start with and really didn't think it was my sort of thing. But the moment I started, I felt an immediate release and I truly believe it helped me to get to a point where I do not live each day in fear and cope with the trauma I experienced. This poem takes you through my experience where I felt trapped and PTSD had a hold on me. I honestly felt like I could not break free. Then it goes onto the part where I did break free and made sense of my trauma, making use of positive affirmations. I believe this will give an element of 'hope'. Things can get better with the right support and people to guide you.

I have even got to a point where I have shared in depth the trauma I experienced in a form of a book. It details my experience with a rare cancer I was diagnosed with at 15 years old and is called 'Beyond Fear Is Hope'. Art in any form is a way of expression, a way for people to see into your world, a way to make others experiencing similar to not feel alone and most importantly a way to release pent up emotions.

## Flight to Freedom Over the Lavender Fields
### Summer Rae Bailey
I have C-PTSD

Carved wire wrapped amethyst, feathers, dried lavender, fairy lights, vintage bird cage.

The vintage style bird cage symbolises the 'trap' of feeling stuck with my C-PTSD but what is inside (at my core) is beautiful...full of love & the hope of new beginnings. This is symbolised by the amethyst heart, feathers & lavender. I have also put fairy lights in the cage so it/I may never have to be surrounded by darkness again.

I also create jewellery. I find crafting, working with natural stones etc very therapeutic. I disappear into a beautiful energy bubble where it's just me & nature's treasures on a wee adventure. There is no room for fear in my bubble.

# How Dare You
## Angela Weeks
I have PTSD

How could you take my good faith, in this Human Race,
and shatter it into fragments.
My mind battered and torn, my thoughts forlorn.
How dare you cling to me: you ugly attachment.

What gives you the Goddamn right, to think you've won this fight.
I am here now to let you know.
Forgiveness is pure and also light; a trophy of my battle's plight.
How dare you dim my golden glow.

When I first encountered you, I was beaten black and blue.
An empty shell of my former self.
Ashamed of my weakened pride, hateful for thinking of suicide.
How dare you make me feel like killing myself.

Who gave you the power, to destroy MY beautiful flower.
The petals now wilted and dead.
In my once glorious alluring garden: you offered no pardon.
How dare you steal the happiness from inside my head.

Why me? I ask on bended knee, Why me? Just set me free.
I wish for you to go away.
Let the past forever be, behind my back... listen, I plead.
How dare you bring darkness to my day.

How dare you? how dare you! one day I will rise,
To conquer my emotions, thoughts and surprise,
you with my strength and passion, once more be full of compassion,
for me, not you.
For I will destroy you like an assassin.

I suffer from PTSD and have done so for over 20 years. This is how it makes me feel on my 'bad days', but there is always light at the end of the tunnel and I will keep fighting.

# My mind transports me to a place I do not wish to go

## Chloe Hunt

I had PTSD and have recovered
through treatment in the form of CBT
(Cognitive Behavioural Therapy)

My mind transports me to a place I do not wish to go,
Why I must forgo this repeated torture I will never know,
A smell, a sight or a sound can transport me,
To a place I do not wish to be,
There I am frozen in terror,
My body shakes and tremors,
My palms are sweaty,
My legs feel like jelly,
My muscles tense, my jaw clenched, hands in a fist,
I am unable to escape or resist,
I try to shut it out and my emotions are masked,
Avoiding everything reminding me of my traumatic past,
Turning off the radio when I hear a certain song,
Turning off the TV when medical programmes come on,
But the door to my terrifying past still bursts open at any given time,
This is why it is so draining living in this body of mine,
Found hiding in the corner trembling in fear,
You may look around and think there is nothing scary in here,
I know it is hard to understand,
But my mind transports me back to the trauma I had to withstand,
It is not by choice, my brain finds it difficult to discriminate between past and present,
Resulting in frequent torment,
I live in daily fear,
As I get over one flashback another can appear,
I try to tell myself I am safe and away from harm,
I try to keep calm,
I try to breathe and get myself to the here and now,
I finally get there somehow,
But my body is drained from the surge of adrenaline,
I am still scared of the demon within,
What is "wrong with you?" people will say,
You were fine earlier in the day,
How can they possibly understand what it is like?

I am constantly on guard I have demons to fight,
I cannot express how I feel or what is going on inside my mind,
It makes it difficult to open up and confide,
PTSD is not just flashbacks,
I struggle to get to sleep,
When I finally drop off I am disturbed by vivid nightmares and my sleep is never deep,
I wake up shaking, scared and drenched in sweat,
I feel a constant threat,
A sudden movement or a loud sound,
I startle and my heart will pound,
It leaves me exhausted and I am no longer who I used to be,
I get defensive and emotional, who could possibly love me?
Desperate to get back to my former self who was happy and free,
I had to speak out and say please help me,
These words are hard to say,
But if you are struggling that is ok,
I have hope in my heart that one day the smile I paint on isn't just for show,
I am brave, tenacious and have more strength than you will ever know.

I wrote this poem to express how it felt to have PTSD and how my mind transported me to a place I did not wish to go. I found people did not understand it, how you can appear fine one minute but not the next. It shows how it makes you feel when you're in the depths of PTSD, what unhelpful strategies you may adopt such as avoidance. Expressing myself through writing and poetry has really helped me to convey to others how it felt to have PTSD and I also found it therapeutic to get it on paper.

Poetry and writing has been an important part of the healing process and writing has helped me to process the trauma I experienced which was related to my cancer diagnosis at 15 years old and the gruelling treatment I went through.

## Searching for Hope
Hannah
I have PTSD

Acrylic on heavy weight paper

I was in an abusive marriage for 9 years, which had contributed to my PTSD. I get frequent flashbacks of the abuse and suffer panic attacks.

This painting depicts the daily turmoil I faced during my marriage. I titled it "searching for hope" because that's all I could do... hope. Hope that one day I would find the strength to leave. Hope for a better future. Hope for freedom. Hope to survive.

# One Moment

## Jo

In one moment, everything changed
The light darkened
The air froze
The silence deafening
Time stood still

That one moment shook foundations
Terrifying, confusing, sadness itself
Shaking, trembling
Throat tightening, unable to speak
Reaching out to comfort

In that one moment, tomorrow became uncertain
Anxiety peaked, a guilt racked mind
Pain filled feelings
Chaos reigned, lights and sounds overwhelmed
Too late to help

From that one moment, eventually a glimmer broke though
Courage was found
Strength developed
Support was needed
Friends and family rallied round

From that one moment, recovery and growth began
Talking, crying, sharing, hurting
Good help taken, the pain ebbs away
Tomorrow begins at last
With love and light and peace

I had one of the worst experiences of my life when checking on a friend I found that she had hung herself. The emergency services were really great in looking after me that night and signposting me to services and my GP. My GP was also incredibly good and carried on seeing me every month for almost 5 years. It's fair to say that in the beginning I used alcohol among other things to try and black out the memories, sounds, lights, feelings and fear that came afterwards….it didn't work. Flashbacks became regular, triggered by blue lights, cold skin, crowds, noise, to name a few and I retreated into myself just waiting for the next one. Anxiety was a huge issue for me as well as 'people not understanding'. But how could they and looking back I'm glad that most people don't. I struggled with work as nothing seemed important. Eventually I was signed off work with stress and depression triggered by the event and for the first time PTSD was mentioned.

I decided that I couldn't carry on living that way and self referred to a counselling service. It took a few months but I started CBT with a great counsellor. I don't know what I expected but I did have to work hard to confront the event and immersion type therapy was primarily used. Flashbacks lessened and each day became slightly easier.

6 years on from the event I still have my moments but so much less. I will never forget the event or the details but the effects of the trauma aren't debilitating or painful. I started writing poetry a few years before the event but it has definitely allowed me to express how I feel about all sorts of life events both good and bad. It can be me or looking in from a distance, it's the act of getting the thoughts out of my head and on 'paper' that helps the healing.

every night when i sleep
I have dreams that make me weep
Every night i find myself reliving that awful day
Every night i find myself running away from what they say
Every night i find myself in a daze that isnt real
Every night i see, hear and feel
Every morning i shed tears
It's a nightmare...
I feel tired of running away from the darkness
It's nothing but a horrible place.. is it my own voice that i hear...
I want to wake, but I'm a prisoner of my own dark world, in my very own nightmare...
I find a light, so far away, but as i reach it, i wake up, its another day. And my nightmare world is gone, until the last ray of light, then maybe into that world, ill have to make another stand, and begin another night where the nightmares will start again.

## Untitled
Jessica Smith
I have PTSD

At the end of last year, I was diagnosed with PTSD, as a result of multiple traumatic experiences.

I'd like to share my journey for the first time to try to tackle some of those taboos and the stigma around mental health. For a long time, I was in a dark place, hiding my pain. Outwardly, I gave the impression I was coping but I was experiencing flashbacks, depression, anxiety, mood swings, nightmares and difficulty sleeping. I started with writing stuff down, putting thoughts into words.

## The Stranger
Matt Hodgetts-Tate
I have PTSD

I stand in front of the mirror and see a stranger
This isn't the face of the person I knew when I was growing up
Something has changed
The youthful joys have gone
Only to be replaced with mournful eyes
The memorise of loss is carried on the shoulders
Like atlas carrying the world.

The face looking back looks lost and confused
Looking for answers to questions that no one cares to ask
The past hangs over like the sword of Damocles
Ready to strike him down with any false step he makes
This isn't me surely I don't let the world get to me like this

Family that he has stood next to when times were tough
When he knew what true friendship was has now past
Yet he yearns for those days again.
To sit in the sun and laugh.
The time when the family was together has now past
Yet the memories of those carefree days linger on.

The memories of long lost civilisations and lands
Have stained this man I see now. Only his brothers
And sisters in arms can understand.
How to explain what these eyes have seen,
What had to be done

He has walked too many miles with the weight of the world
For too long has he yearned to explain
For too long he has spoken to deaf ears
The ungrateful surround him
Too quick on their rat race life to judge

He looks back at me preying for the day where the darkness
Of the past can be pierced by the light of joyfulness again
I look back and remind him to look out for the angels
That protect him each and everyday
For once he smiles!

This poem was written at my lowest point, I'd lost a good friend in Afghanistan, my marriage had broken up and my black Wolf had taken over.

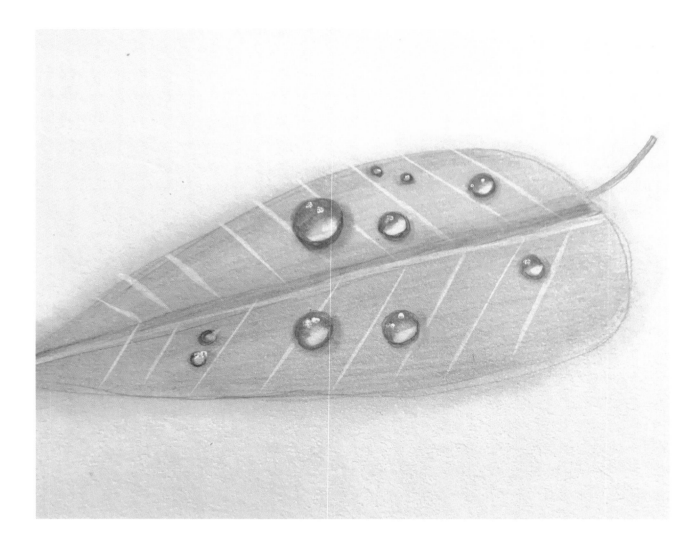

## Healing
### Debra Purse

Pencil

This is pencil drawn and it means 'Let your tears fall and blow away with the wind.'

## PTSD and Me
### Evelyn
### I have C-PTSD

Childhood neglect and abuse
no one for support,
Early thoughts of being
so bad and unloved

With no one to trust
and learning early
suppressing emotions
was how to survive

Hurts and injustices
polarities and paradoxes
No one to turn to
confusion reigned

Quiet and shy
feeling angry inside
Sitting in the shadows
silently watching

Trying to play the game
but not knowing the rules
I was on the periphery
I didn't fit in

Feelings of unease,
night after night
tossing and turning,
and sleep evading.

Chilling night sweats
exhaustion pervasive
the struggles faced
just to get out of bed

The light of day,
only dread lay ahead
with heart pounding
chest tight, hands dripping

(continued overleaf)

The phobias started
life's such an effort
with boots of concrete
being dragged behind me.

At work I would fake it
the mask would appear
that smile on my face
the class clown is here

I could fake it no more
life lost its lustre
Nothingness
the world stopped

No meaning to life
I took to my bed
I didn't want to be here
I was lost in my head

A story of hope
where I felt none
it had all gone wrong
something had to be done

With trepidation
I entered therapy and
today, years later
I live life well

The road I travelled
it was not easy
but I found me
and 'me' is not bad

The world is out there
with everything to offer
a place for me
where I belong

I have courage and
now I look up
I see the world again
in all its glory

I embrace the
love around me
breathing it in
and feeling its warmth

It took a long time but
I want to be here
and most of all
I enjoy being....ME!

I decided to write a poem about C-PTSD, the effects this had on me and the way I am overcoming it, to inspire others.

I had no interest in poetry until one day after a therapy session I started writing and rhyming what I wrote, although this poem is free verse. I found free verse helped me to see how things really were for me and this allowed me to feel the emotions I had been suppressing.

I find art very therapeutic, I also sing, draw, paint and take photos.

I sit on the brink
swinging back and forth
so painfully to do
so painful to see

mania setting in
grasping my soul
my body
my breath
what do I control

the questions fade
As it stretches for days
within a limbo of crisis

loss of sense
touch
with reality
riding the manic wave
inside your brain
where no one sees you drowning

the need to run
isolate
f*** this hate
I need your touch
I can't give up

Your body a narrative
Hard back, spine cracks, lines but only one paige
A glimpse of your journey just not unscathed
Your story continues, your learning, your growing your shifting shape

You now the author
You write your own book
shown within your skin
so perfect so rough

Your soft lips, spoken words
beautifully read never unheard

wounded by words
shot from your sharp tongue
You're more than your reflection
You're becoming one

Hoping one day you'll see yourself
the way I do
so beautiful, so whole and so incredibly you

# The blend of life
## Paige Bartram

Writing is an explosive tool to release, unite and resist.

Words hold truth, they have power and help navigate the self.

It is daunting putting pen to paper, thoughts to words, never apologise for the way you take up the space.

Writing is scary, it's empowering - it encourages us to face and conquer our fears, which is what I am here to do.

I am here to face my inner fears, build my self confidence and creatively express myself.

Having such a relationship with words can be difficult: brutal honestly is hard but finding the strength that pushes you further than you ever thought, dreamt possible - and if you didn't have that dream, that's okay too, things do get better.

I believe in you.

## Crushed
### Shannon Workman
### I have PTSD

Sketched initially with graphite pencils, coloured with charcoal pencils and soft pastel sticks and then defined with a ball point pen

Crushed is the best word for how your life changes when coping with the effects of PTSD, flattened is how you feel, your life has been totally derailed and you have no idea how to come out the other side or how get it back on track, it's hard, but I honestly came out the other side a better version.

Granted it was the hardest journey I will ever take and it took a long long time, but the new me runs much better than before, more self aware, more understanding and more empathy for the struggles of others.

Life can be totally flattened by PTSD, its confusing, scary and you often wonder how you can ever unfold the pieces and get back to 'you' again. Well, after being 'run over' by a truck, you cant really, you can restore most of the parts, but some dents will still be visible.

I think this piece says it all really, what PTSD feels like, the impact it has, how it sometime's stops you in your tracks and can leave you feeling totally and utterly crushed.

Now this might be metaphorically speaking in regards to the picture, but it represents the crushing effect that PTSD can have on a person and their life.

# At Sleep
## Kelly Williamson

It comes scratching, scratching at my door
This thing of silent shadow
It rears up like a monstrous sea serpent
Setting its intentions on a helpless ship
A terrific roar rips from its throat, ear splitting
As it crashes down to obliterate the doomed vessel
This thing of rage it twists and turns, this reeking choking mist.
Its knarled bony hands bare the scars of a thousand ill deeds
Stinking grave dirt clings and long dried blood stains
All broken finger nails and time worn joints
Clawing and grasping, blindly reaching for its prey
The darkness favours it, shrouding its features
Its hideous form enveloped by a silence only the stars know
This abominable creature knows no rest, drifting endlessly
It wears its sins like a cloak, all black anger and velvet
It creeps and slithers forward like a dark cloud alive
Drawing ever closer made more ominous by the sound of a ticking clock
It seems to threaten, seems to speak although says nothing aloud
Words so vicious and cruel, heart splitting accusations
Unrelentess and determined, it pours its venom and bile to drown me
Words so damaging and painful, soul destroying rebukes
This devil of the dark has no pity, no soft side, empathy has no home here
There is no payment or penance it will accept, nothing to halt it
I have feared it so, at night in the dark, at day surrounded by others
Its always there, waiting, forever waiting until I am too weak to fight
I uncovered it once, pulling back that black velvet hood, finger tips burning
I chose to believe I was at sleep, dreaming wildly of monsters and demons
For the face I was staring at in such fright, was my own.

I find writing can help with my C-PTSD. When I am struggling with my mind I find writing helps to slow my thoughts down and it allows me to express the pain I am suffering. I often read over my writings and find myself amazed and proud that I not only survive such feelings but I can overcome them too.

## Untitled
Sian
I have PTSD

PTSD for me was a result of a difficult pregnancy and birth experience. I have since struggled with flashbacks and anxiety around my daughter's health.

For me, photography is a way of capturing special times and memories. This picture in particular shows me how happy and healthy my daughter is but also how far I've come.

The slogan on the jumper adds to this message and it is definitely a photo I will look at on those bad days to remind myself that we are happy, healthy and safe and tomorrow CAN be a new day.

## Torment
## Jess Cody
## I have C-PTSD

Ballpoint pen on paper

My artwork is very personal and important to me.

Since 2018 up to the present I have been looking at intergenerational trauma, traumatic incidents and areas of conflict within my work.

I began by focusing on the decades of conflict in Northern Ireland. Beginning this journey at eighteen years old I did not have the confidence to address my own trauma outright although it is clearly represented in my images.

Stigma and the lack of a diagnosis held me back. Since then I have been diagnosed with C-PTSD (complex PTSD) which has allowed me to address my trauma in a more direct way.

Along with the support of my consistent and patient Art Psychotherapist over the last six years and my GP, I have grown in confidence addressing personal illness and infection, the deaths of close friends, childhood traumas along with my relationship with my therapist.

When my mental health struggles became more severe I found I was unable to create. Thankfully, I have picked up art materials and started creating again from mixed media, sculptures, printmaking and pencil drawing.

Artwork gives me a focus when nothing else helps and is a way I can proudly represent myself for both the world and myself to see.

## The Storm Will Pass
### Cecilia Bryant
I have PTSD

Digital - on iPad using 'Procreate'

**SECOND PLACE WINNER!**

Art has always been a coping mechanism for me and something I've always enjoyed since I was little.

I went through trauma at 4 years old and art has been like a lifeline.

This picture signifies the struggle of anxiety, stress and overwhelm that I've had to deal with for most of my life. But hope is there and it is what has kept me going - I feel like though dark feelings linger, there's still light on the horizon. Though stress is part of me, it doesn't define me and I am still there when the storm has passed. Through the midst of it, I survive.

# Breathe
## Natasha Harsley
I have PTSD

Breathe!
That is what you tell yourself; again, and again.
Breathe;
Like the weight of the world is not sat upon your shoulders.
Like you are not crumbling more and more with each passing moment.
Breathe.
Through the Night terrors; through the flashbacks that freeze you to the spot,
Breathe.
They tell you to calm down. They tell you to just get on with it;
Little do they know that you try and you try and the frustration within makes you crumble all the more.
Breathe.
Tomorrow is another day. Tomorrow is another step closer to recovery.
Breathe.
You are not alone. You are never alone.
Breathe,
and smile as you take each little step, at your own pace; in your own way.
No matter how long it takes you or however many miles you have yet to go.
Breathe.
You are not your illness; you are so much more than how it tries to define you.
Breathe.
Shout out each little accomplishment; each milestone you make and know, that YOU are worth so much, no matter how broken you may feel.
You are not alone; there is always someone who knows how you feel – who understands.
So just, Breathe.
You are worthy of it!

Breathe is a poem that I created from my own experience with PTSD and people around me who don't quite understand what it is that is going on - or the struggles PTSD sufferers face. Sometimes we often forget the simple act to just breathe; to breathe and take a moment to regather ourselves when things get too much. I hope that this poem is a small reminder to anyone else who suffers that we just have to breathe and remember that we are all worthy.

## You See
Samuel Humphrey

'You See' is a response to the confinement I now often feel as I come to some kind of terms and learn to deal with PTSD.

As you learn over time talking about PTSD (causes and symptoms) can feel hard, relentless and alien. This diptych reminds me of posters for some kind of freak show. Even with those clearly sympathetic or open to listening there can be a feeling of being very exposed and trapped.

Painting has become a very powerful release for me. Though some of the imagery is dark looking at works I have produced at the end of a difficult, or even average day gives me hope and belief in myself.

## Memories
### Gemma
### I have C-PTSD

My life's a tiring journey
And I'm waiting for the end
Because I hope that you'll be there
My one and only friend

You were here some years ago
Standing by my side
Helping me through right and wrong
Watching me with pride

You were the maker of my smile
The destroyer of my tears
You understood my silent thoughts
You calmed my deepest fears

I thought you'd always be there
You were part of every day
My going out, my coming home
Until you went away

Did you ever wonder who I'd be?
Or what I'd do in life?
Did you ever wonder what you'd miss?
Or to whom I'd be a wife?

Where did you go when you disappeared?
Did you go to a better place?
Are you out there watching over me?
Putting smiles back on my face?

Or am I here all on my own
With no-one to look after me?
And am I smiling at just memories
Of my Grandad smiling back at me?

My childhood was very difficult and very abusive. It wasn't until I was 39 that I was diagnosed with C-PTSD. During my childhood, my grandparents were my source of strength. My Grandad passed away from cancer when I was 11 years old and after this point, the abuse from my mother got even worse. I tried to remain positive by telling myself that my Grandad was still keeping a watch over me, although at times I found this difficult. A few years later, I found that it helped to put my emotions onto paper and I started to write poetry. I wrote this poem when I was struggling with thoughts about where my source of strength had gone.

# The Red Hours

## Helen Mills
I have PTSD

Permanent marker, colouring pens and colouring pencils

My artwork means personal physical and mental anguish but also closure and strength in adversity. It is a raw image of my PTSD that enables me to come to terms with trauma.

I drew this at university and rather than distressing me, depicting my suffering in a picture allowed me to confront difficult, often overwhelming feelings.

This drawing has helped me to overcome the personal heartbreak, humiliation, alienation and weakness I have endured.

Through the vivid use of colour, I have been able to face head on the potency of trauma.

I can reflect on this artwork always and remember the courage I had to draw it. Art remains so vital to me in my ongoing therapy.

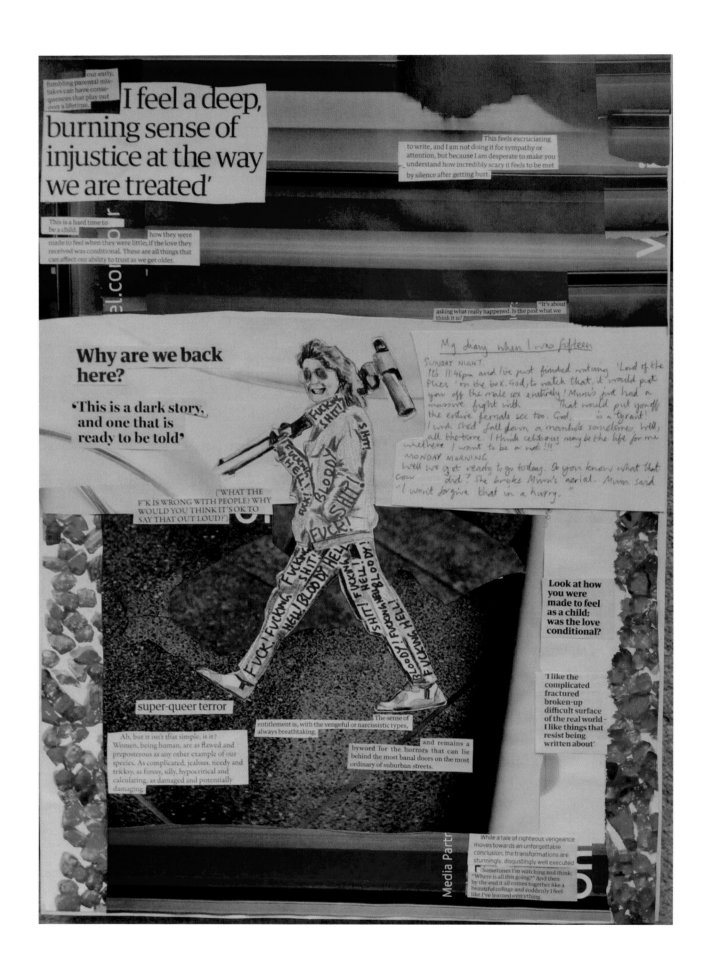

# Untitled
## Abigail
I have PTSD

A3 mixed media picture, using collage, newsprint, Sharpie pens.

My artwork is a picture of a bullying, malevolent presence in my life: I was bullied and treated with contempt and disinterest. I was unable to speak out or reach out for any help. I kept diaries from an early age and so I included a passage from my diary in my art.

My PTSD was such that I learnt to minimise myself, to be small and silent, to swallow down my feelings of hurt and to just try and get through my life until I could move away to university. And PTSD made me forget the worst excesses, and so in researching this piece of art, I came across another example of her aggression and included it in my art. The image of her is covered in swearwords because she spoke like a docker, using filthy words at us in anger all the time, and as a result I am quite mild mannered and rarely ever use swear words in anger.

I make art to assert myself, to allow myself to be angry, after a childhood where I was not allowed to be angry and I spent all my time scared of the angry people around me. Making this art helped me to find peace with myself and it allowed me to actually express some of my own feelings of anger. I felt much better afterwards.

Ignorance kills

PTraumaticSD - a loss of trust and connection

## slow death from ignorance
Beverley Booth
I have C-PTSD

Small Watercolour - photographed then text added

I am not damaged I'm traumatised and misunderstood - I live in survival mode because I only have me to protect me.

My watercolour is to show that you need to take care of a plant otherwise the plant will die because you gave it no care or understood its needs. People need the same care and understanding. Everything in life needs connections otherwise it dies slowly.

Ignorance of others, can destroy a person who is trying to heal and reconnect. Like a plant we need to trust to flourish. Otherwise our roots will die and hopelessness appears.

Darkness enters and the world becomes a lonely, scary place, then we die.

## Helpless
## Karen Hughes

Watercolour

In 2018 my sister passed away and I used Art to help me with my grief. I paint my emotions and life events to express how I'm feeling. Art has helped me heal and help others along my journey.

# Self-Acceptance
## Rebecca Clinton

Acrylics on a ¼ inch thick piece of wood

Before we can move on we must accept ourselves.

I'm not good with portraits but I did this one of myself. It doesn't look much like me, but I'm happy with the result.

Whatever life throws at you; it can lead to a very distorted view of yourself. In order for me to start my healing process, I need to accept who I am, and that I am valid, my feelings are valid, and there is nothing wrong with my tastes and my looks. My body is the shape it should be. It doesn't matter what people think, because I will never know, and does their opinion really matter? My husband loves me regardless of what I look like. I can be me, and its time I accepted who I am, and live my best version of me!

It was a really hard piece to start with, but I dug through my self-confidence issues. As I looked in the mirror and tried to paint what I saw, I was over critical, and the painting looked as sad as I felt. So I told myself a new mantra - you have the strength - I put my positive face on. The painting changed from a sad face to a happy determined one, once again finding my inner strength to get through all this.

Painted in acrylics on a ¼ inch thick piece of wood. With a mirror in front of me, and using only my brushes to manipulate the paint, I let the picture almost create itself. Using the mirror only as guidance in the end, I painted myself in a way that looked right. Somehow, it is so different from how I look, and yet I see myself in it and think perhaps, I'm not used to seeing myself looking so bright, happy and determined.

## Untitled
Tanya Robertson

This signifies hope through acceptance.

Most of the painting is colourful and celebratory, flowers that light up like candles, starbursts that mimic fireworks.

This painting evolved from first expressing the blue side of my feelings, dark, lonely, messy frustration layered thickly from the perspective of lying in the mud. Only then did I focus on making pretty sky patterns and adding flowers.

It's about finding a balance.

## **Caged Beast**
Jesse Cather-Long
I suffer from C-PTSD

Photography

Sometimes having PTSD can feel like a beast is caged inside of you. But you just need to remember, all beasts can be tamed.

Kamran the Lion at Bristol Zoo

For me photography is a way to show the world that some people see it differently, I love to show people how everything can be seen from different angles. Photography is an escape from the world and an escape from my mind.

It Would be too easy to say that I feel invisible.
Instead, I feel painfully visible, and entirely ignored.

**Untitled**
**Kate Battye**
I have PTSD

Spray paint and homemade stencils

This is a quote I found on the internet and I have illustrated it in a literal way.

A SMILE CAN MASK THE PAIN, BUT, THE EYES SAY WHATS HIDDEN

## Listen to the Eyes
Shannon Workman
I have PTSD

It's true that eyes are the windows to the soul, they can sparkle when happy but look empty when they echo sadness.

My eyes were empty for years, if they did reflect anything it was sadness and fear.

I would stare in the mirror, over and over, looking directly into my own eyes and be totally consumed by how 'lifeless' they looked.

I wondered how long it would be until someone noticed, until someone helped me?

It took me a long time to realise that I was already looking at the only person who could help me and that was me.

Once I realised that it had to start with me, I found the voice and courage I needed to ask for help, then and only then slowly things started to change and I've never looked back.

They say the eyes speak if you only choose to listen and that eyes can often reveal whats going on within a person. This is both true and also something you fear, because as much as you want to run away and hide, you also want someone to see how much you need their help.

I always felt my eyes gave me away, no matter the smile, no matter the words, when I looked in the mirror, my eyes always screamed "help me", but the question was 'could anyone else see it too?'

Smiles can be painted on, they are easy to fake and can make a person 'look' happy (even when the reality is so so different) but the eyes always seem to know the truth.

Its quite therapeutic to see this piece down on paper, these are my eyes, my words, my pain, my battle and its one that I can and will win.

# Grounded
## Rebecca Clinton

As the world moves on around us,
The seasons swirl about us,
I dig new depths, and stand my ground
Until better days surround us.

The sunny days seem gone too soon,
And lovely nights I spent under the moon,
Seems all too soon taken away,
Before not so long the days are short,
and the skies have turned to grey.

From nowhere it seems, the wind hits hard,
And the good days are now long gone.
I put my head down, brace myself,
For the onslaught that's coming along.

I may drop my leaves, look dishevelled and lost,
I may be a shell of myself,
But what you can't see, are the roots that I grow,
that makes me much stronger than most.

For my feet are grounded deep,
I know my purpose in life,
Every time that I am threatened,
I grow from that bitter long strife.

When the bitter winds go,
and the darkness resigns,
I let out a sigh of relief.

For here I am,
I have survived yet again,
survived, and my life re-aligns.

The light does return,
I lift up my head,
I stand tall once more,
and look where life has led.

I unfurl my new leaves,
and survey my surround,
the skies are bright,
and I stand strong in the ground.

I'll enjoy the new days,
the new branches I've laid,
and deepen my hold on the world.

As time will keep trying to push me back,
I will keep my new strength and be bold.

Written to represent the continuous waves of torment that life throws at us, whether still going through trauma, or reliving in the daily life of a PTSD sufferer.

For me, I became afraid of being happy, as I was always preparing for the next blow. So many and so often through my life has been the pattern that it was safer to shut down my emotions in order to survive. It still rings true for me now as I work through my complex PTSD issues, as it represents the storm that hits us when triggered once more.

H.Karenina 2018

**I breathe in my courage and exhale my fear**
Heidi Kjelstrup-Johnson

Pencil and digital art combined

Art is my saviour: It keeps me grounded, it gives me a voice and through my art I have discovered a positive outlet and a healthy means of expression.

## Battling the Storms
John Howcroft

Acrylic

Battling the storms, waiting to subside, worst storms inside, bathe in lightning, amongst the darker troves, windswept and drenched, a thirst for life unquenched, I endure these storms, unbending and eyes raised, dancing across the waves and become the storm (represents the endurance of the human heart in life's storms)

## Vortex
## Rebecca Clinton

Acrylics on a ¾ inch thick piece of wood

My paintings give me understanding of where I am, where I am going and how to get there.

This painting is over a meter tall, so I felt like I was spilling my feelings out onto the wood beneath me (I paint mostly on the floor).

The swirl of emotions that continuously surround me, the oblivion that will engulf me if I don't stay strong, my strength in not being drawn in to my end. It would be easy to let myself fall, but I haven't battled against it all this time to give in now.

Paintings like this show me I still have the strength to push on. Exhausted though I am, I CAN do this.

Large piece painted in acrylics on a ¾ inch thick piece of wood. No pre-planning – Using only my hands and brush to manipulate the paint, I let my emotions lead the colours and movements that created this piece.

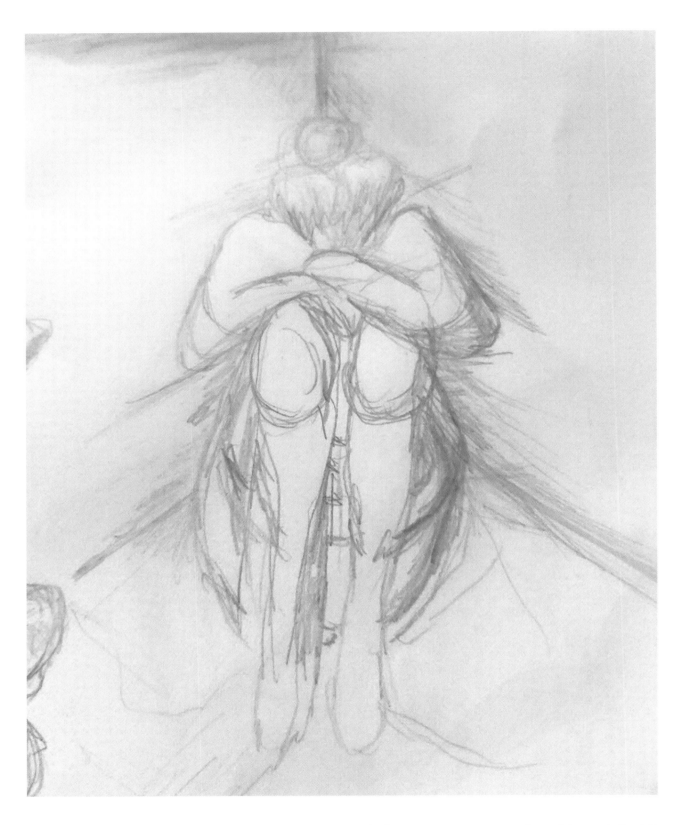

**Untitled**
Paula Evans

Art helps me express my thoughts as I find it difficult to talk about how I feel.

## Untitled
## Melanie Ainsury-Panesh
I have C-PTSD

Over the years, due to complex PTSD, I have found it very difficult to communicate verbally. I have found that with the use of my drawings, I can communicate much more effectively.

This drawing explains my difficulty with slow understanding, my worries about losing vital documents, etc, always carrying everything around with me, to back up my lack of verbal communication.

Like a snail, I crawl through this frantic life, struggling but surviving.

# Love grows from the wilderness around us
## Rebecca Clinton

Acrylics on a ¾ inch thick piece of wood

This one is about life that's happening right now. The symptoms of PTSD nearly destroyed my marriage. In 2020 I had almost made my mind up that we were to separate, we have had problems throughout but have always got through it. I was blaming my husband and his problems, for most of our issues.

Only later in the year, after having a breakdown, and being diagnosed with PTSD did I start to realise the extent of issues I was causing, and how much was my doing.

As our relationship has gone on, I have pushed him further and further away. He is very supportive now we know what's happening, as he can see I am trying to come back to him.

When we first met, I was already broken, and I didn't realise just how much I was living with on a daily basis. We formed our love from a bad place, and our intimate relationship has never been easy.

Now through all the tangles of confused emotions, I am learning to love him once again, but slowly, in a way that it is only him in my head, rather than my past fighting against it.

Painted in acrylics on a ¾ inch thick piece of wood. No pre-planning – Using only my hands and brush to manipulate the paint, I let my emotions lead the colours and movements that created this piece.

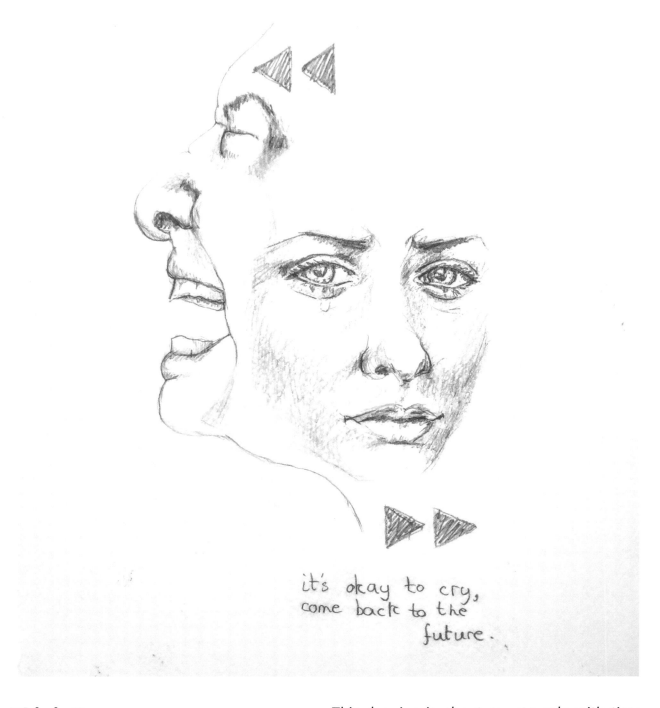

it's okay to cry, come back to the future.

## This is Now
### Nadia Henning

Pencil

This drawing is about my struggle with time, memory and the emotions of the past in my everyday. Bringing myself back into the present, accepting my emotions and focusing on the future isn't easy, but drawing and artwork help me work towards that.

# Zombie
## Andrea Ballance

I exist in an undead zombie state.
Alive on the outside, other living humans relating only to my surface.
You would hope I was dead on the inside but I am not.
I am perpetually dying. Dying but never dead.
In every day, in every moment.
Some moments filled with terror.
The best moments, numb sleep.
Most moments, eternal burning...
but I never die...
Never dead, but isolated. Alone.
Fighting an exhausting war, defending myself from triggers.
Triggers that intensify pain and separate me further from any vapour of love that might actually reach me.
Would love heal me?
A tormented ghost, haunting my old life.
I used to love...
but now I exist in an undead zombie state.

At the height of my PTSD I was, like my poem explains, totally lost, walking dead. I can't explain it, even now, but I remember being haunted by loneliness and distrust. I couldn't trust myself to make healthy decisions or to trust the right people. This meant I couldn't go to a therapist. I was physically exhausted. I would suddenly just drain out and have to go to bed right then and there. Even in sleep however, I never recharged and felt refreshed. I felt like people were separate from me, mainly because they could never understand what terrible emotional, physical and spiritual pain I was in. It was total loneliness compounded by my own lack of ability to deal with my overwhelming emotions that often drowned me for days. I was a void where hope and love was. A void waiting to be triggered and turned into a tsunami. After many years I tried the Boulderstone Technique. This was the only therapy that had any real effect on me. It slowly melted my emotional overwhelm and I didn't have to do lots of talking about the past. It was right for me.

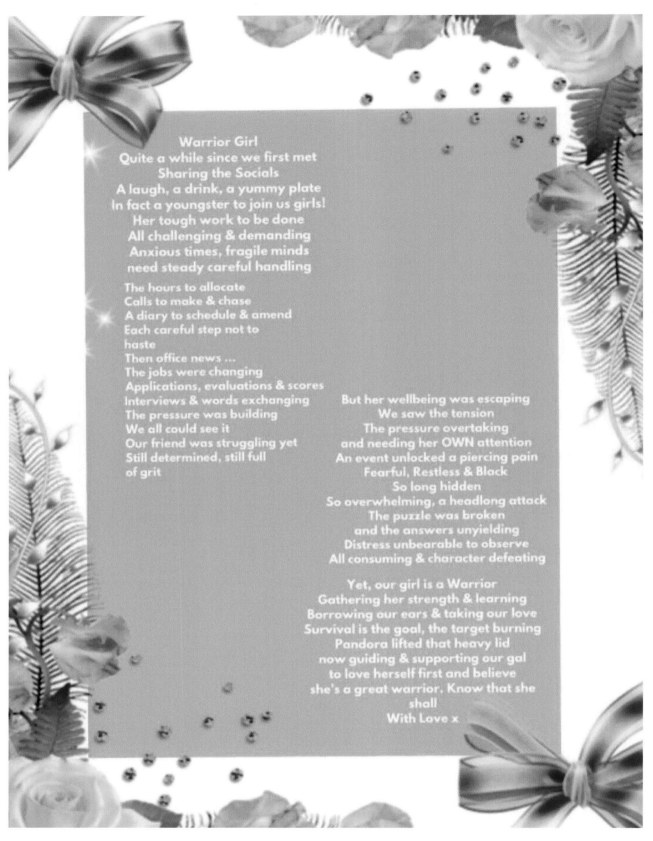

**Warrior Girl**

Quite a while since we first met
Sharing the Socials
A laugh, a drink, a yummy plate
In fact a youngster to join us girls!
Her tough work to be done
All challenging & demanding
Anxious times, fragile minds
need steady careful handling

The hours to allocate
Calls to make & chase
A diary to schedule & amend
Each careful step not to
haste
Then office news ...
The jobs were changing
Applications, evaluations & scores
Interviews & words exchanging
The pressure was building
We all could see it
Our friend was struggling yet
Still determined, still full
of grit

But her wellbeing was escaping
We saw the tension
The pressure overtaking
and needing her OWN attention
An event unlocked a piercing pain
Fearful, Restless & Black
So long hidden
So overwhelming, a headlong attack
The puzzle was broken
and the answers unyielding
Distress unbearable to observe
All consuming & character defeating

Yet, our girl is a Warrior
Gathering her strength & learning
Borrowing our ears & taking our love
Survival is the goal, the target burning
Pandora lifted that heavy lid
now guiding & supporting our gal
to love herself first and believe
she's a great warrior. Know that she
shall
With Love x

**Warrior Girl**
**Tracy for CeW66**
My friend has PTSD

A view from someone looking from the outside in. Showing the changes that take place.

## Dark times lightbulb moments
CeW66

Copper Work

This is one of the first creative pieces I completed during the very beginning of a very dark time for me.

The grey item is a hydraulic valve from a Vulcan plane. I made this lamp for a friend to show there is light for us all. How my life changed at a flick of a switch

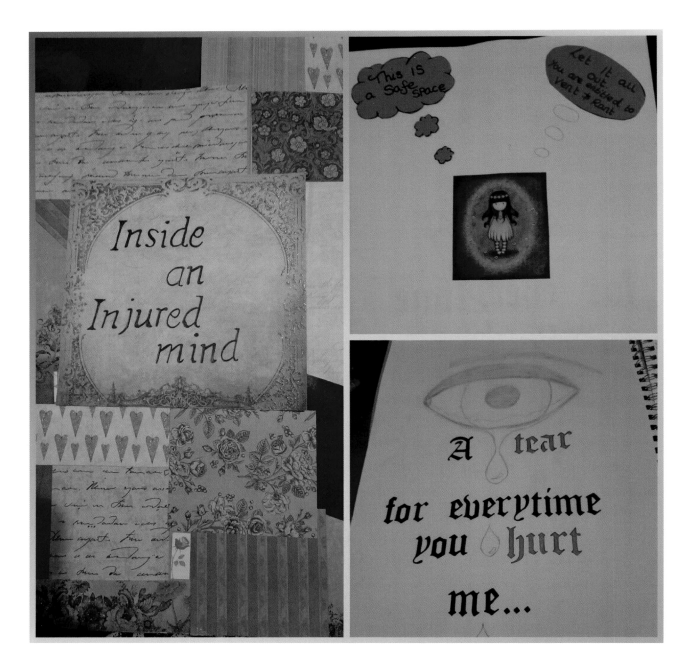

## Inside an Injured Mind
**Francesca Clay-Bolton**
I have C-PTSD

Pencil sketch and card craft on paper

This book is a work in progress that I made as a tool to safely express my thoughts and feelings without fear of judgment.

Having this outlet allows me to manage my symptoms, explore/process emotions and practice focus and mindfulness. This book gives me control over my mind and allows me to ground myself and work through flashbacks, memories and triggers safely.

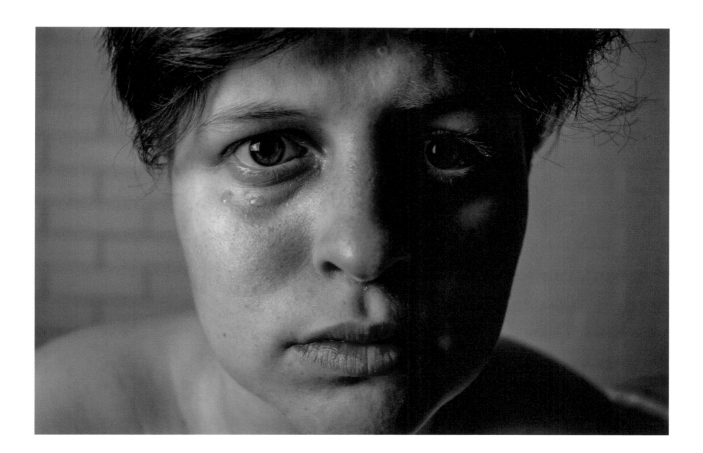

## Silent Tears
Jesse Cather-Long
I suffer from C-PTSD

Photography

In many cultures crying is seen as repelling the negative energy out of your body. Sometimes, all you need is a good cry to help get rid of the negative emotions and carry on with life.

This is a self portrait.

For me photography is a way to show the world that some people see it differently, I love to show people how everything can be seen from different angles. Photography is an escape from the world and an escape from my mind.

# Family
## Sharon

When your family look at you and scorn
When they see you battered and torn
A dark look in your eyes
Once again, no surprise
You feel more pain, twice the load
For your family as well as that toad

When your son hears your cries
And he clearly sees the pain in your eyes
You try so hard to make things right
You don't want him hearing this fight
You feel more pain, it mounts up high
When you think of it all, all you can do is cry

When your father feels your pain
You look at him, gaunt and drained
You smile all the while, putting on your face
He arrives, your clothes scattered all over the place
You hide this fight and also your plight
Your pain however shines out like a light

When your mother no longer wants to know
Even though you have nowhere to go
She turns her back and can't believe
Her daughter is gone and she can't retrieve
She sees your pain in every day
And can never understand why you stay

All these ties served to heighten my pain
The pain of abuse, feeling slain
My family is hurt, These feelings so acute
Not even sure I still love this brute
But time goes on with more abuse
To keep the peace, I call a truce

I was eventually, after many years of impossible and constant symptoms, diagnosed with C-PTSD by a trauma therapist. She said I have exhibited one of the clearest cases of C- PTSD she has ever seen.

I spent far too many years on the receiving end of a controlling and abusive relationship, and ignorance on the part of GP's to not even know how to look for trauma in an individual has , without a doubt, exacerbated my symptoms as I've carried them around for years not knowing what was wrong with me.

I wrote this poem because I am by and large a home bird. Although, as a young girl I wanted to travel more and thought working in a big city would have been exciting for my life experience. I didn't get that chance. I had my son at 18 years old and went 'out of the frying pan into the fire' a few times in respect of relationships. Over time I became very proud of my Home town and it's people. Working people as my family all are. I built a successful business there.

I had to make many many very difficult decisions as I became a young successful woman despite the problems I encountered along the way. I always felt safer in my home town where I knew like the back of my hand, when in fact I may well have actually BEEN safer had I lived that earlier dream and moved on and away as a young woman. It's funny how the mind can play tricks on you, if you feel safe it doesn't actually mean you ARE safe. I now know this.

The flip side of family being close by did mean that often I would close my eyes to make my very very difficult choices in life, while often, I was dealing with all hell breaking loose at home and at work. Hoping that I wasn't being judged by this same family. My family. I found it impossible mostly to describe my difficulties in life to them , for fear of judgement and being shamed.  My poem is looking at the bittersweet feelings of having your family being near which can help at times, but sometimes not, as your life and hidden difficulties play out near those who sometimes judge. That's a very narrow and hard road to travel. It takes its toll.

## Nightmares
### Clare Reece
I have C-PTSD

Canvas with acrylic paints

C-PTSD affects me in many ways. I suffer insomnia, and when in do sleep I have horrific nightmares. I'm easily startled, which causes panic and anxiety attacks. I struggle with people, I'm agoraphobic. when I do go out, I can't go anywhere busy. I can zone out, I struggle to balance my emotions. I'm currently receiving EMDR therapy, which is starting to make a difference.

This piece of artwork is called Nightmares. I have horrendous nightmares every night, some are flashbacks, some are like they've been directed by David Lynch. I find the best way to deal with the nightmares is to paint them otherwise they linger for days, increasing my anxiety and hypervigilantcy worse.

I use art to express my nightmares and emotions. Painting is great to escape daily life and just zone into.

## Cuckoo
Samuel
I have PTSD

'CUCKOO' is a piece I painted in response to the incident where I developed PTSD.

My house and life were invaded by a gang over a few months. It was an extremely life threatening and challenging time. In the end I literally had to flee for my life. The name given to this surprisingly common incident is 'Cuckooing'.

The surrounding buildings in the painting have no doors and no-one is watching which represents the isolation I felt during this time and after. It seemed no-one understood or could offer me physical or emotional sanctuary.

The Cuckoo in the picture is invading a Robin's nest as I have a very special affinity for these birds. Putting one in a Robins nest is a way of acknowledging how deeply I was affected, and still am by the things that happened.

## Hope
### Edit Biro-Hannah

I work with people who have PTSD & C-PTSD to help them overcome their traumas

Acrylic, foam board, plant, soil, sunlight, and photography

The tree is a universal symbol found in many spiritual traditions. It represents many things such as wisdom, strength, beauty, and regeneration. In art and art therapy, it may represent the self. It also represents humans as we develop roots, strengthen our trunks and branch out to a wider vision of life as we grow.

In my image, I placed it in a white gallery where it broke through the ground, growing its first new leaves towards the bright light. It reaches skyward, and it has no boundaries as it is capable of breaking through even the toughest walls.

Experiences of extreme trauma can leave one speechless or rather not finding words to express the feelings, emotions and bodily sensations that follow the event or events. My image embodies post-traumatic growth and was inspired by my own journey of healing from trauma.

I don't know if I had PTSD, perhaps a little. But after surviving 7/7, I utilised the arts to heal. I mean all forms, not only visual arts. When I had the experience in 2005, I was working as a costume designer-maker for television and theatre. As an immigrant, my English was not good enough to express the feelings I was going through. Then, I realised no language is good enough to express trauma but through the arts where a sense of distance can be created through metaphor and imagery.

My strength and my resilience got me where I am today, and I am extremely proud of my achievements, and I would love to inspire others.

## Floating or Sinking
Hattie
I have C-PTSD

Acrylic paints

It's an expressive piece showing the sense of floating and numbness that C-PTSD gives when your brain dissociates.

# Let sleeping dogs lie
## Marie Cooke

How can they say let sleeping dogs lie
Do they not realise I would love to try
As I lie in my bed at night eyes wide awake
Hoping and praying there may be a break
That tonight may be the chance for a decent nights rest
But no once again nightmares are my guest
Over and over all through the night
Tossing and turning reliving the fright
Then morning arrives and I crawl out of bed
To face the day again and filling with dread
Hope the mask stays in place and that I don't cry
So I can pretend to them all that I've let sleeping dogs lie

I wrote this a while ago to try express how I was feeling, people just say get over it, don't think about it, it will go away but they don't understand how can you when it is always there and you feel you have to hide it behind a mask to appear normal. It has helped me to express without having to have awkward or difficult conversations

## Garden of Sins
### Anonymous
### Recovering from C-PTSD

Her body froze and her vision blurred. Time slowed down, moved back and forth, round and round, up and down until it just stopped. Everything died, the plants lost life and the ground was dry.

He'd flipped the switch of the sun and every light went out. Clouds disappeared and stars burnt out.

The earth stopped spinning. Radio silence. All that remained were disturbed flashes of film her head caught on tape. the violation of her decency sickened her to the core. "Is it my fault?" she asks, because her heart is gold and his is cold.

Her innocent mind too sheltered to comprehend the upside down of manipulation and abuse. But how could it be that she is the one bleeding guilt when it's he who should be sat amongst the weeds in his garden of sins?

Little does she know, karma will reap what he's sown.

For me, poetry is a way of expressing myself, in ways I can't verbally when it comes to trauma. I wrote this poem to signify the emotional impact on a rape/sexual abuse survivor and the internal conflict that survivors are burdened with. It meant a lot to me to be able to put my traumatic experience into words that I hope may help fellow survivors to feel less alone in the turmoil.

## Dandelion
Emma HS
I have PTSD

Photography

PTSD made me feel fragile and vulnerable. I never knew when the next flashback would come, or where I'd find the next trigger. But through EMDR therapy I started to find my way back again, and I am starting to feel more like me.

## Behind the mask
### Julie Green

Acrylic, various cuttings from music sheets

I'm an Artist and Charity worker. Inspired by nature and I love to recycle old music sheets and books. Creativity keeps me mentally healthy and I hope it will encourage others going through uncertainty.

## The Senses
### Stephanie Brant

Watercolour and ink on Paper

A simple sight, smell, touch, taste or sound,
Is enough to bring them here.
It is not as if I invite them in,
Smile, talk, sit for a while,
Then offer them some tea.
I have no desire to entertain them,
Yet, as always, here they stay.
Treating this mind like a hotel,
Coming and going as they will.
Oh dear Flashbacks, Intrusive Thoughts,
Please do find, alternative, hospitality.

## Yokai
## Laura Ducker
I have C-PTSD

Acrylics on paper

I am 34, and severely visually impaired. I have a narrow tunnel of usable vision.

My painting, done in acrylics, takes inspiration from the Japanese legends of 'Yokai' (spirits or demons) who possess, trick and hurt people- as C-PTSD/PTSD does.

I find that painting helps me distance myself from mental anguish, and feeds me with strength to keep going down a dark forest's path - even when the wolves circling in the darkness try to pull me backwards.

The woman in my painting is deliberately bright - she may be on her knees here, but look how far along the path she is already - she keeps going.

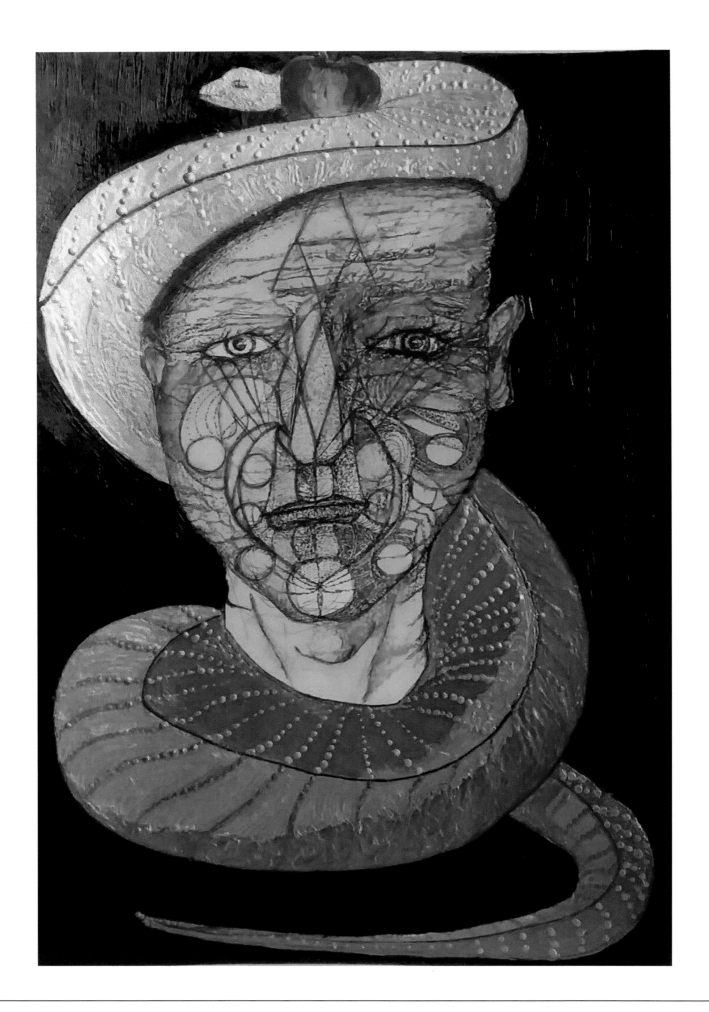

## Naja
## Maria

Oil, copper acrylic, silver acrylic and ball point pen

This is a painting representing my dad, who caused a lot of my trauma as a child.

The snake represents his sin, but also my trauma which makes me feel strangled from the neck up.

The lines on the face are to represent traumas universal links and how we all really are just one being trying to free ourselves from the traumatic pasts of others. It to me seems endless.

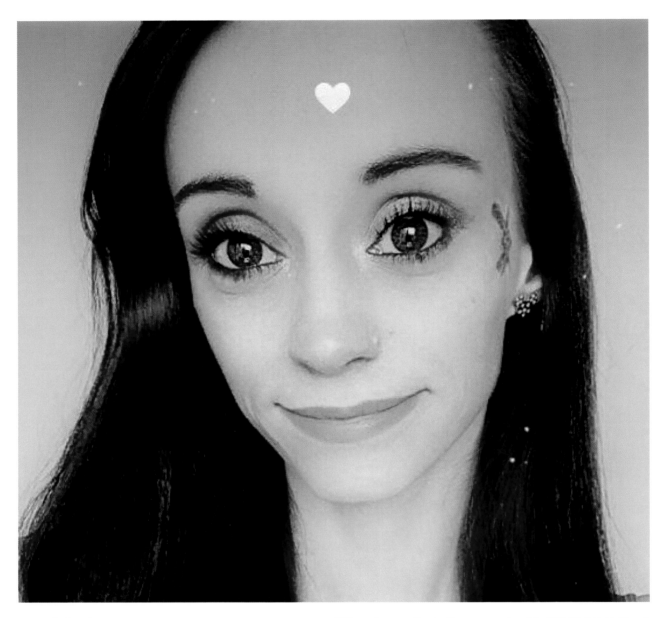

**Untitled**
Michaela Harris
I have PTSD

Make-Up artistry

When I was first diagnosed with PTSD I felt like I had invisible chains placed upon me, this was my own personal life sentence of hell! It took me a while to accept it but with the help of my children and my bf I started trying new things to find something that would help me manage everything.

This eventually brought me to makeup, my makeup is essentially my warrior paint! Everyday is a new creation and when I stand back and look at my work finished I get such a sense of pride and I feel strong, beautiful and more confident!

My face truly is my canvas I created this look to show my support for others like myself fighting this demon that is PTSD!

## Untitled
## Tanya Lunn

Quilting

My stitched work represents the fragments of my life that I hold together in silence...the flower Garland represents hope for the future...

# The Prison Within
## Shannon Workman
I have PTSD

Sketched initially with graphite pencils, coloured with charcoal pencils and soft pastel sticks and then defined with a ball point pen

PTSD controls you through fear and its the fear that keeps you trapped: real fear, perceived fear, triggered fear, memories, thoughts and dream fear, imagined fear, fear of the unknown, but also fear of the known. It's so hard to live with constant fear and you end up trapped in a cycle of not living at all....your mind traps you inside your own body and that's no way for anyone to live, the only way forward is to escape any way you can.

I have called this piece 'PTSD, The Prison Within' as this is a literal picture of what you might see if you looked inside someone with PTSD, its my feelings, my mind and my thoughts.

Me, trapped inside a literal prison inside myself, with the bars made from my PTSD, and me, looking through those bars, longing to escape but not knowing how or where to even start.

Although PTSD is a 'invisible' prison, its very very real to the sufferer and they often feel they are trapped within themselves, it has a real 'locked in' effect on a person and although invisible to everyone else its just as hard to figure out how to escape from.

There are so many levels to PTSD which are represented here by the addition of the handcuffs as well as the bars themselves.

A person might escape one aspect of the 'Prison' but that does not mean you are actually free. It takes a long time to unpick the 'locks' on the handcuffs, to break down the 'bars' and then to escape the prison walls to finally allow you to feel free from PTSD and from The Prison Within.

## Untitled
Abbie James

This is a canvas I've been drawing, that has kept me busy throughout lockdown. I've not had much time as I have 3 young children, it's been difficult, and this had helped me to cope with things.

To me this picture represents 'yin and yang', and how they go together, good and bad, love and hate, sadness and happiness. I believe they all go together, in perfect harmony, I will keep going on like my drawing does.

## Untitled
## Pamela Jordan

The long path of loneliness and misunderstanding to open the door to normality and happiness.

# Phoenix Rising
## Fred Mayer

Time to talk, time to tell
To tell my truth, to the tribe
Gathered here in this sacred space
Where the ancients spoke before
Where the children will do one day
In their turn, in their time

The hollow man, the broken child
Joined at last, reconciled
Fusion fire fills my brain
Melted down and forged anew
In that crucible of pain

The prison walls
Are broken down
Shattered shards of the hall of mirrors
Scattered all around

A new day dawns
Seen through new eyes
Spread these new grown wings at last
And reach towards new skies

I wrote this poem a few years back, after becoming aware in my mid 50's that there is a thread of C-PTSD reaching right back into my early childhood. It's about the pain of breakdown and disillusion, followed by the joyful release of new insight and ultimately the hope for recovery.

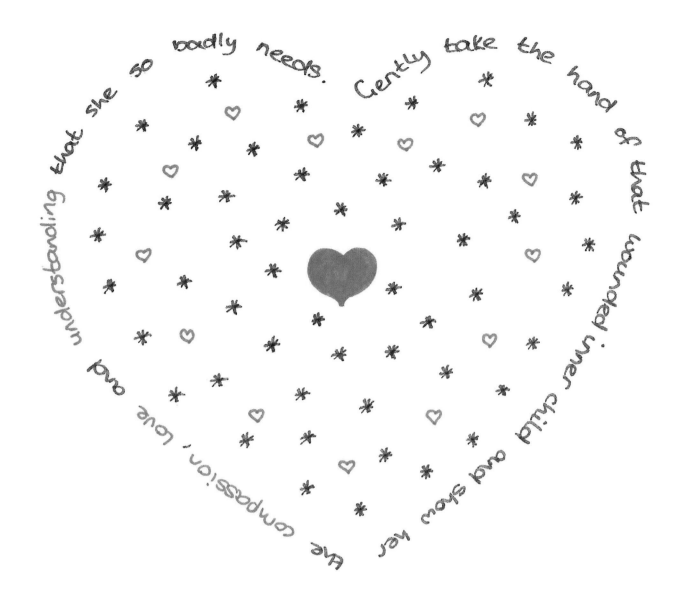

Within the heart, handwritten text reads: "Gently take the hand of that wounded inner child and show her the compassion, love and understanding that she so badly needs."

## Heart of Compassion
Nicky Taylor
I have PTSD

Fineliner pen

I am a survivor of childhood sexual abuse. I created the 'Heart Of Compassion' during a really dark time when I was struggling with PTSD as an adult.

The hearts represent the age I was when I became traumatised. The stars represent hope. The words were what I needed to hear. I felt so desperate but realised that I had the power to reach out and comfort my wounded younger self. She deserves all my compassion, love and understanding.

I will always be here for her xx

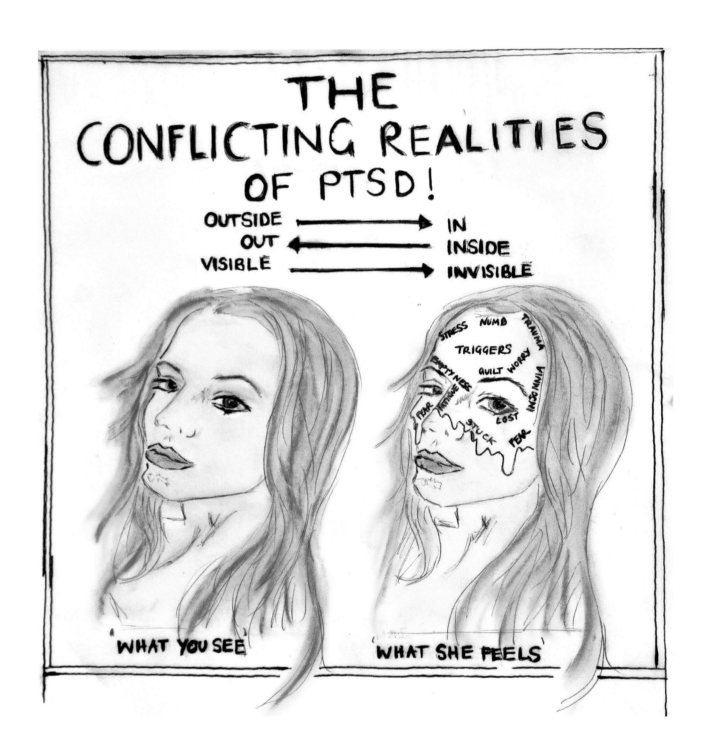

# Turmoil
## Shannon Workman
## I have PTSD

Sketched initially with graphite pencils, coloured with charcoal pencils and soft pastel sticks and then defined with a ball point pen

'Can you REALLY see me?' This question is a honestly a double edged sword. Having a mental health condition (despite much more understanding in recent years) is still very misunderstood and something we mostly fear.

I've managed to function without question through periods of self harm, depression and PTSD, functioning the whole time whilst hiding it from a world that fails to understand, hiding it through fearing both the stigma and judgement that can be attached. Wanting to both hide away and also be seen can cause so much inner turmoil, its just so confusing, as at the same time as hiding you are also really really hoping for and needing someone, anyone, to see the real you (as only then can you move on and heal) its such a constant conflict as you want to stay silent but also want scream it out loud.

If the inside and the effects of the trauma were visible on or through the skin, I often wondered if people would walk away in fear or stay to understand more.

How a person looks to you (and to the world), is more often than not absolutely nothing like how they actually feel on the inside. Just because a person has got up, got dressed, made themselves presentable and decided to face the world does not mean that they are not also fighting an inner battle that the world knows nothing about.

I've often thought, if people could take a peek inside and actually see what someone was feeling or what they were thinking, would it match up to the outside that you can see or would they be shocked at the reality of the turmoil thats hidden inside? More often than not they would be shocked at the conflicting reality between what they see and what or how someone actually feels.

Its the visible against the invisible, we are often blind to other peoples feelings, but imagine if to really see the truth we only needed to peel back that outer layer. Would you want or dare to look?

On the flip side, would you want anyone to look, it can make you feel really really vulnerable to reveal whats hiding within, but revealing the within is often the only way to calm that storm, ride it out and get to less choppy waters.

## Untitled
### Katie Nicholl
### I have PTSD

This piece of art work was created to express some of the thoughts I have personally. This is how PTSD has affected me from past experiences and I thought others could relate to this too.

I feel like it's still seen as a subject people are ashamed of so it's very out my comfort zone to do something like this. However, doing this piece has taken my mind off of everything and I was able to create this without being overwhelmed. It signifies how at your lowest times there's is a cloud that's flooding you with emotions but the "I'm fine" speech bubble is to show how a persona is put up so people don't worry about you. This is what needs to change as people should feel like they can reach out without feeling judged.

Lurking in the shadows
In the landscape of my mind
Are the memories of the trauma
I'd rather leave behind

Just like you I'm only human
But my mind's a complex mess
And some days I feel defeated
By my Post Traumatic Stress

## Lurking in the Shadows
Charlie Forsyth

PTSD has affected all aspects of my life since childhood and throughout my adulthood. Some things I have gradually got better with, I am less affected by loud noises but I can still be quite jumpy, and certain images of videos can trigger me. Relationship wise, it has made me push people away in the past and even now I have trust issues, - when things get tough my first instinct is to distance myself. I am very lucky that I have a supportive and patient girlfriend who understands how PTSD impacts me, and I am surrounded by some amazing friends and family.

I find writing poems cathartic, after many unsuccessful years of therapy for PTSD, I find writing helps me process and portray how trauma has affected me.

## Triggers - Fight, Flight or Freeze
## Shannon Workman
I have PTSD

Sketched initially with graphite pencils, coloured with charcoal pencils and soft pastel sticks and then defined with a ball point pen

Triggers are something you have to learn to ride through (they are often unexpected and can be things far far from the obvious).

Just when you think you have learned to cope, a new one will strike and the cycle starts over again.

When they strike, you are initially 'paralysed', gripped in the jaws of fear, you freeze, every trigger, every time, your heart pounding and your body shaking.

To learn to overcome the fear of when triggers strike is the main goal of therapy, the fear response is lessened and its the fight response takes over, you learn to ground yourself in the present, breathe through the fear and calm the mind.

You learn to recognise that you've been triggered and to see that in that moment the 'perceived' fear is actually just an echo from the past.

This piece is my own interpretation of experiences with PTSD (as it can be an 'absolute monster')

PTSD can pounce at any given moment. When triggered, there's no warning, no time to prepare, and even something seemingly innocent can trigger it to 'bite' and take you 'under'.

The flip from absolute calm to sheer panic (which can happen in a split second) always reminded me of the tranquil and serene calmness of when a deer is tentatively drinking right at the edge of a waterhole, and then the absolute ensuing panic and chaos of when the crocodile surges from the water and triggers the deer's fight, freeze or flight mode and its then a fight to see who escapes.

Triggers are difficult to overcome but with therapy, coping mechanisms and with time, you can learn to manage and even calm the effects of when triggers decide to 'pounce' and even as the 'deer' you can actually learn to stay afloat instead of being overwhelmed and taken under.

# The Cutting
## Hayley Porter
## I have C-PTSD

Life...
It can cut so deep
I have no other words to speak
Of this heartbreak inside

My dripping tears
Fall down my cheek
Showing the heart ache inside

I'm broken,
I'm so upset by the unspoken
Please relieve me
I can no longer try

I'm done,
Once it's done it's done!
No stepping back
Our lives have just begun

I'm numb
Shake me from this place
I'm numb
Someone shake me
I'm done

I'm ripped up inside
It cuts so deep inside

The cutting
My darling
The cutting
Please stop the cutting
Please stop the ride

The cutting
My darling
The cutting
Please stop the cutting
Please stop the ride

Everyone says they know best
Little do they know?
That we know what's best

It's our secret
A Hidden meaning between you and I
One that we can't deny

And now we're gone...
Happiness is so near
I feel it
The cutting is gone

The cutting
My darling
The cutting
Please stop the cutting
Please stop the ride

The cutting
My darling
The cutting
Please stop the cutting
Please stop the ride

And now were gone...
Happiness is so near
I feel it
The cutting is Dead!

The year of 2015 was a year I would never forget. I had a full-blown mental breakdown and was eventually diagnosed with Complex PTSD & Bipolar Disorder. A Friend of mine who's a practicing Musician helped me through this difficult time and taught me how to channel my thoughts, emotions and feelings into Creative Art-Work. At times I felt engulfed by incredibly difficult emotions and although I was reluctant at first, I became very inspired by this to turn it into a creative talent: Poetry & Creative Writing. The emotional release was beyond belief and I eventually found myself becoming impressed by the work I'd created. It taught me how to channel negativity and turn it into something positive.

I could feel my confidence growing daily and this gave me a reason to fight back and with the right support allowed me to understand the different parts of me that I'd created through past trauma's. It gave them a voice. No longer was I or them silenced. We were noticed! This helped me to transition into the person I am today. You have to start with your own blank canvas. It's not easy but why not become your own Creative Art Work and become something you're inspired by and truly proud of?! I hope my piece brings inspiration to some of you in time. Thank you for reading. :-)

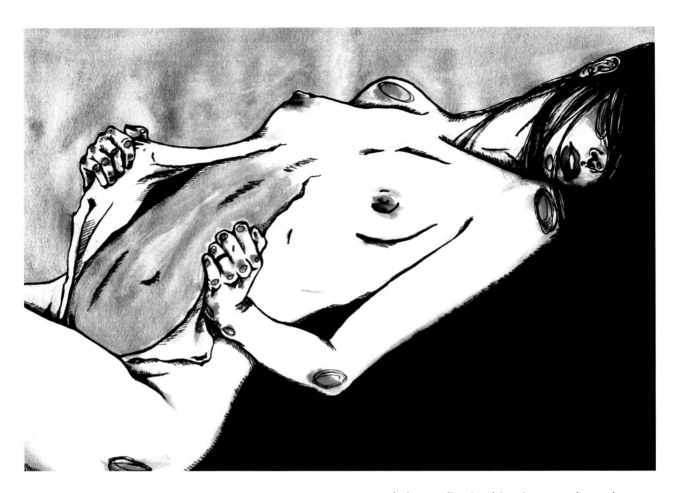

## Continue
## RefuseTheBox; Millie Hardy

Micron pens, HB pencil, ink and acrylic paint.

I wanted the nudity in this piece to show the raw vulnerability included in the healing of PTSD/CPTSD.

It was my intention for the subject to be conveyed to be rising from the darkness, and in this process opening themselves up to the new; by the literal shedding of one's old self. I thought exposing the stomach first would show the strength and trust in the submission to their personal journey.
As they shed their 'old self', they leave behind the darkness, no longer enveloped but able to see from an outside perspective the journey they have so far taken.

The physical shedding of one's self symbolises the growth of the subject, from the consuming darkness representing C/PTSD and trauma, perhaps different, but no less beautiful than before. It also gives the subject control of their transition and a balance between negative and positive; represented as light and dark. Reminiscent of Ying and Yang.

They look back in acknowledgement of the darkness of their past, with an undercurrent of fear of the unknown, but hope for the future.

**Moving Forward**
Jo-Ann

This signifies peace stillness relaxation - that is so important, yet rare in my day to day life.

## Interference
## RefuseTheBox; Millie Hardy

Acrylic paint, inks, Micron pens and HB pencil.

This is one of the first pieces of art I made in direct relation to my experiences of C/PTSD.

I have studied art and made lots of pieces that whilst expressive never really felt like my personal expression. I felt so much confusion and interference when I was coming to terms with everything. I hadn't created anything in such a long time after the initial diagnosis due to the symptoms and I felt like my world had come crashing down as though all my experiences had gathered together and syphoned all my creativity (even though during my traumatic experiences I used creating as a form of escapism).

After beginning therapy and having some reflection I braved picking up my equipment again and this piece was created.

I feel like this was a rebirth for myself and my creativity and since then I have been using that creativity to express myself and relate to others after isolation, I really feel that using art to raise awareness for mental health struggles is important because art is much easier to understand than most other methods and it can open up relatable feelings and emotions between one another. Its perhaps even humanising after my personal experiences created threats in every person I saw.

I don't create as often as I like and its certainly isn't a cure all for me but it's something and that something is better than nothing as I thrive for clarity and healing.

## Untitled
### Dawn Camplin

Machine Embroidery

My picture signifies my family, the hand is showing care. I might not be able to have control of things outside of my house, but I can control the health and safety of those around me.

I designed this image on paint 3d and then machine embroidered it. I got the machine in June and I had never digitized or used an embroidery machine before.

**Untitled**

Jemma Swainston-Rainford

Everything on my door step and all the skills able to do it but the trauma holding me back

## Unspeakable
### RefuseTheBox; Millie Hardy

Acrylic paint, inks, Micron pens and HB pencil.

With this piece, I was initially trying to communicate the struggle that comes with C-PTSD. The raw negative emotion that can be experienced after having a particularly bad day.

However, as the piece developed, I feel as though it is showing more than the negativity associated with C-PTSD and trauma. I feel it's strong and empowered, with an undercurrent of feeling and emotion that can change depending on your current situation as you view it. I think it maybe even shows a sense of personal conviction that comes with the process and a compelling beauty.

It holds importance to me because it reminds me that this is how C-PTSD can be; layers of complex emotions with a cycle of ups, downs and roundabouts and certainly not something I should feel alone in or ashamed of.

I feel it's worth sharing with others in their own battle, to give strength and comfort in knowing that we are not alone. With it I hope it can help friends, family and acquaintances to understanding what we are dealing with and help to express and relate difficult feelings, emotions and experiences with one another, whether dealing with C-PTSD or not.

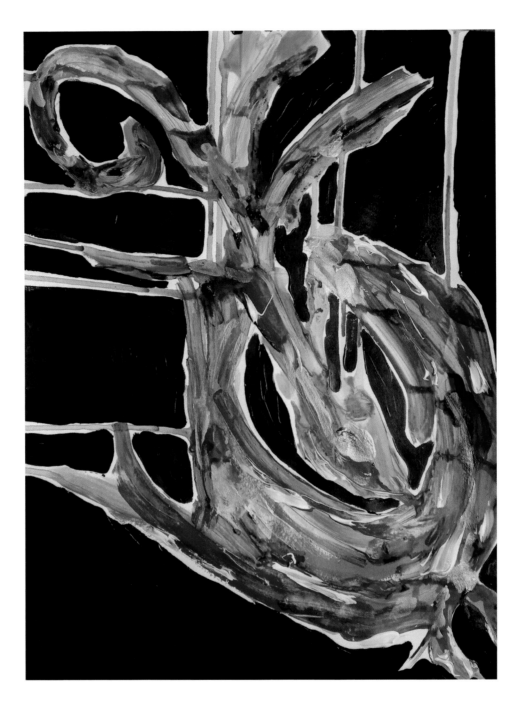

## Untitled
### Elizabeth Cornelia

Acrylic on paper

I dealt with physical and emotional trauma all through my childhood and this has affected me throughout my life.

I always sought chaos because it felt familiar but I've ended up in some dangerous situations because of it and using substances to block out the pain. Now I have been in recovery for 1 year and I am getting the help I need in order to make sense of my trauma and live a fully functional life.

Sometimes putting one foot in front of the other still feels difficult but I can always see the growth in my work.

## In sickness and in health
### Nadia

I do, my love, I do,
But only while you're well,
If you suffer mental illness,
I'll halt our wedding bells!

I do, my love, I do,
But only while you're fit,
If you develop mental illness,
I'll leave you in the pit!

I do, my love, I do,
In health but not in sickness,
For if you have mental illness,
It seems there's no forgiveness.

I do, my love, I do,
'Til death do us part,
Just don't let your brain get sick,
Or we'll never get our start!

I do, my love, I do,
But the world still shames and frowns,
If you suffer mental illness,
They'd have me let you down!

To hell, my love, to hell,
With all their hypocrisy,
In mental sickness and in health,
I'll be the light for you to see!

My partner began to develop mental illness as a result of burnout from caring for me. I had often told him to leave me, to "save himself" before I took him down too. When he began to display symptoms I realised how I couldn't leave him now that the situation was flipped. I wanted to support him as he has done for me... not out of duty or debt but devotion. When we devote time, love, patience & effort to coping and healing, we can walk together towards the light, despite what perceptions society might have.

I paired the poem with a photo of a rainbow I captured on a rainy sunny day because I enjoy the juxtaposition of the painful subject matter with the hope of recovery that's possible with the right support and tools.

Poetry and imagery has been a major coping tool for me, especially when I find myself disassociating.

## Escape
## Lotty Lee

Acrylic on canvas

I had become unwell with postnatal depression after my first child was born, but there was more to it, lots of historical trauma was surfacing and it was coming into my reality.

It took a while before I realised the way I felt was not right, then when my daughter was 18 months old I was at my wits end and finally reached out for help from my GP. This is when my recovery journey began.

Once this treatment started I began getting this vision of a safari adventure, an adventure I wished escape to. I had already painted before this time but I knew this vision was meant to be placed on canvas.

I brought the Acrylic paint, canvas and over the next 18-24 months I created "Escape." As well as having support from therapists I have found that Painting can be my therapy of choice, it gives me the opportunity focus on something constructive with a proud outcome. I feel like all my anxieties disappear when I am painting because I am all in / focused / committed to this piece of art. I love being creative and sharing this with those I love.

## The World does not look right and things do not seem real
### Heidi Kjelstrup-Johnson

Photography combined with digital illustration

I struggle with ADHD, PTSD and dissociation which at times feels like a losing battle. Art gives me a voice and a means to express myself. Through my art I am able to express what I fail to achieve through words.

Life has felt very disjointed as of recent as I have struggled to adjust to my new surroundings BUT I persevere despite the challenges faced. Through a tremendous amount of effort, often faced in a sheer state of panic and disconnection, I have somehow managed to build up enough courage to travel to and from work without the disabling panic attacks.

Through repeatedly having to face my fears I have began to build up more resilience and this is enabling me to stay within my window of tolerance, and therefore, avoid slipping into that frightening dissociative state where the World does not look right and things do not seem real.

© 2020        PTSD in the time of Covid-19        Philippa H Curtis

## PTSD in the time of Covid-19
## Philippa

Acrylics

I experienced over a decade of physical and psychological abuse as a child.

I struggled for decades with OCD, anxiety, and depression. After a number of crises which impacted my physical health significantly, I was diagnosed in early 2020, with Complex PTSD (Complex Trauma). I've had several years of counselling as well as treatment involving EMDR and art therapy.

This piece was my first art therapy attempt and I was trying to represent my hyper-vigilance, my neural pathways firing constantly, and the impact that C-PTSD has on all areas of my life and my body.

The black blobs are my terror/anxiety who I named 'Itsy Bitsy'. Originally my terror/anxiety was a black, cancerous network with tendrils pervading all of me. Itsy-Bitsy is less frightening and more contained which allows me to talk to him and have more control.

## Untitled
## Keith Baddams

Glasswork

Having been brought to tears during the pandemic whilst watching an interview with an NHS nurse soon after finishing her shift on a covid ward , I could see in her eyes the trauma she was living with every day and wondered what images she saw when she closed her eyes.

In the glasswork I decided to close her eyes and pixelate her thoughts. Since making this piece, I approached NHS charity "Doctors In Distress" and it will be auctioned at a fundraising event in May 2022.

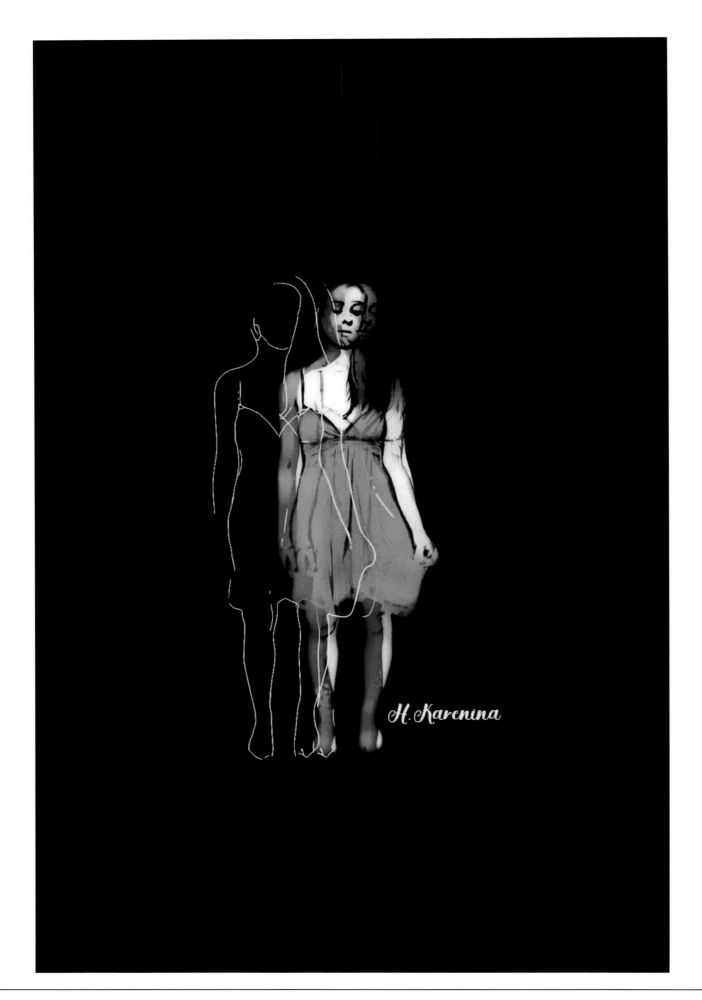

H. Karenina

# Mixed states
## Heidi Kjelstrup-Johnson

Photography and digital art combined

"I never thought it would be so difficult to reflect on my emotions. They confuse me greatly and I struggle to remain consistent. I feel like I have different functions: different emotions, thoughts and feelings and for different situations and with different people but they are not connected."

The more that I learn about PTSD and dissociation, the more that I am able to understand the reasons behind why I do the things that I do, why I think and feel in the ways that I do and why I act and react in the ways that I do. As I understand more about the human mind and how our brains have been developed and designed to 'survive', the less 'crazy' I feel. My experiences feel validated and I feel better understood - I AM NOT ALONE! There ARE people who genuinely understand, who experience the same physical and emotional experiences as me and who HAVE been able to get the right help and support to move forwards with their lives... so that means I can too I guess...

Now that I finally feel safe - I have managed to reground and I am back within my window of tolerance. For those who have experienced trauma you will be all too familiar that the window of tolerance often becomes quite narrow, especially during times of crisis! I have spent the past month in a state of crisis, my mental state has fluctuated between hyper- and hypo-arousal and the dissociation has swung into full force, but today, today I feel alive. For the first time in a very long time I feel a sense of of connectedness. My vision is clear, sound is 'normal' and the colour is back!!!! I am still consumed by a heavy tiredness that pulls at my eyes, my head and my shoulders like a heavy anchor on a boat pulling me down to the depths of the ocean. This constant feeling reminds me that I am still attached to the traumas and they still hold their heavy grip but at least I am back into the realities of the World and can think more logically, more coherently. I am me again - the 31 year old adult seeking for change. Fighting for justice. I am no longer that scared, traumatised 14 year old desperately searching the streets for a place of safety.

## The Key
## Kara Shepherd
I have PTSD

Acrylic on canvas with ink detail. Hemp ash background and few dog hairs in honour of my dog Mia who has be been my rock through everything.

This is the first serious painting I have created for many years. Due to my mental health, lack of funds and a hectic life I rarely have the time to paint. In creating this, I realised how much I have missed painting and I was encouraged to paint more.

I am a photographer (this is my most active creative pursuit) and community art tutor, so over the years I've just done small personal projects or projects with my art students but nothing on this scale. I have suffered with PTSD for years, but for the past year I have been in therapy using EMDR treatment. Painting this was creatively challenging, as well as cathartic as the subject is so personal to me. I found myself really enjoying it and stayed up to all hours painting. Art in all forms has always soothed me.

In my painting everything is symbolic of my personal journey with PTSD.

The slightly skewed composition relates to my distorted view of the world due to my PTSD.

Merry-go-round - I have lived in the merry-go-round of fear for so long, round and round with no way of getting off the horse. Over the years it has slowly crumbled as I heal and go through therapy

Words in hair - My symptoms of PTSD.

Black negative space - The darkness surrounding me and creeping into every corner of my once free spirited mind. I wondered if it would always be this way.

Red eyes - Paralysed by what fresh fears lurk and haunted by horrors of the past. What obstacles lie ahead, will there be another trauma I have to survive.

Multiple eyes - Stuck in perpetual limbo, too scared to move forward but terrified to stay still, with the torrent of demons coming behind me. Forever waiting for the next attack! I have to be incessantly vigilant, never able to rest my exhausted soul.

Red pulse - Heart palpitations and panic.

Clock - Distorted mind, distorted time. Trying to heal too quickly, take your time and in time, all will be as it should.

Scales - Pining for some sort of balance!

Dove & Unalome - Peace and Enlightenment is coming

Gold veins - I strive for light, I fight with my fire and the light soon breaks through

Keyhole and golden path - The light at the end of the tunnel is near just keep breathing and keep moving forward

Key - I am the key to my own life, my own healing and my own happiness. I am in control, I hold the power

# Chilled
## John Howcroft

Watercolours and chalk

The images in the clouds represent love, faith and life with the heart angel and dolphins presented in this piece as clouds.

It is done in watercolour, with a chalk sky. It incorporates real nature salvage in the design, with sand from Ballygaley Beach used as well as seagrass and the daisy tattoo is real daisies with braided twigs from the same location (a place special to me and where I can breathe and be free from all the issues that close in).

This is the poem that accompanies the piece:

"We measure time in smiles,
in vivid arcs of rainbow,
curving gently to touch the sea,
left shimmering upon rhythmic tidal wave,
to caress that golden shore,
time suddenly becomes no more,
than a mere inconvenience,
as we embrace under the bluest sky,
upon this ancient Rock a naked sigh,
in a communion of intimacy our love ascends, until the afterglow of sunset ends,
awaiting of return to reality"

Without this blessing of art and poetry this last year, I would be in a much darker place.

## Hope
**Katie Larvin**
I have PTSD

Digital Art

This piece of artwork was created after an EMDR session. I have never had a drive to create a piece of artwork before but I just felt that the image in my mind of how I was feeling needed to be put onto a page.

For me it symbolises the disparity I feel within myself. The inner child of Katie still feeling strong but locked in by the fears, hurt and horrors caused by others. I hope that it is seen as a symbol of hope; we are still in there.

I don't like writing or reflecting on my feelings so art & music has been my saviour. They capture moments.

## Healing
### Savanna Mackay

Out in nature with flowers

This heart signifies the self love I've gained since completing therapy.

I used flowers to show the beauty that can come after the rainy days, also dandelions can withstand a great deal of force and pressure just like me!

I created it outdoors in nature where I can always ground myself when I feel low especially the fact I forage and exercise which helps me clear my mind of any stresses.

## Just Breathe
## Vik Revelle
## I have C-PTSD

The world starts to pixilate,
Sense and logic evaporate, dissipate.
I am transported, teleported, distorted.
Memories imported.
My mind contorted.
Hairs stand on end, skin starts to crawl.
Eyes wide open.
Loud noises smother me, bury me.
Sweaty palms. Feeling dizzy.
Descending, Spiralling.
Grasping, gasping, clawing, jerking.
Losing my grip, I struggle,
Slip and trip, stomach flips.
Feeling sick.
On my knees, drowning.
Shivering.
Scared.
Crying.
Shaking.

STOP!

BREATHE!

Breathe!

Breathing, seeing.
Breathing, feeling.
Breathing, hearing.
Breathing, smelling.
Breathing, tasting.
Noticing, breathing.
Grounding.

I'm OK, I'm here, I'm back.

I often feel misunderstood. I wanted to write something that would help people understand what it can be like to experience PTSD from my point of view. I hoped to capture the sudden debilitating and complex nature of these episodes. That said, I also wanted to demonstrate how sometimes they can be managed and their impact lessened by simple grounding techniques and mindfulness.

## Stop!
### Jemma Furnival

My head feels like
it's going to pop.
I don't want to die,
I just want it to stop!

It's a heavy, aching,
sickening dread.
A medicine ball in my gut.
A swarm in my head.

My mind spins and wobbles,
I just want it to stop!
This merry-go-fucking-round,
- I want to get off!

I'm an old kind of tired.
I'm ready to drop.
I've tried for so long,
I just want it to stop.

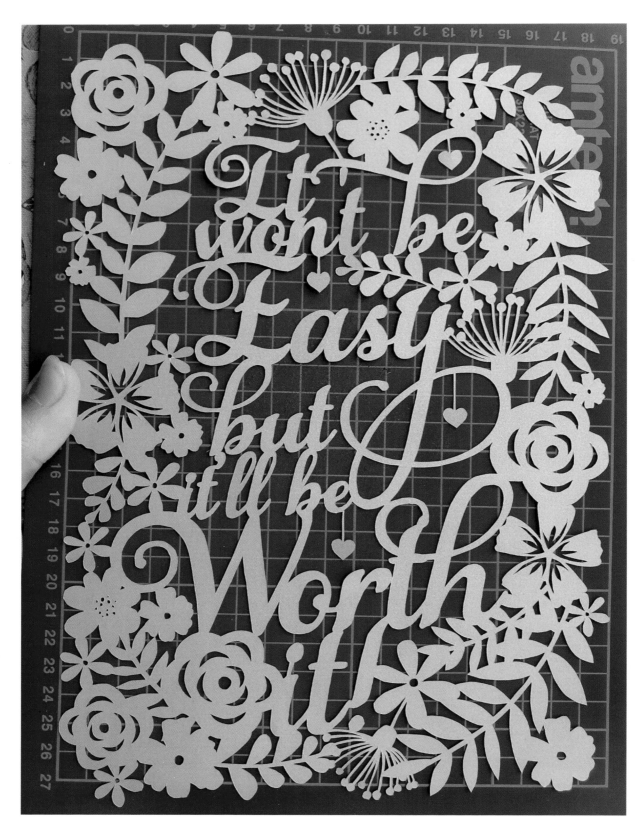

## Untitled
### Kayleigh

Hand cut paper-cutting using pearlescent paper and scalpel

Crafting has been a major part of my recovery after being emotionally/physically/mentally and sexually abused by my ex-partner. This phrase really sums up the whole journey I've been on. It isn't easy what so ever, but it will absolutely be worth it in the end.

## For my Son
### Silviy
My son has PTSD

In a world full of lies
a mother's heart is bleeding.
A world her child despise,
a world he finds hard living.

A child with unsung virtues,
who gave up on divine rewards,
a child who shunned all vices,
a slave to pain and swords!

The secret, silent, mother's love
that reaches far beyond his feelings,
shelter in a raging storm,
past flows and meanings.

In a world full of lies,
a mother's heart is bleeding.
A world her child despise,
a world her love is healing.

I have written this poem for my son who suffers from PTSD. As most of you will know, talking to someone with PTSD about own feelings could be painful. Especially, if this is your parent. The poem expresses my feelings, however the main aim of this poem was to tell my son that I understand and that it's ok. And I will love him regardless and unconditionally.

## Trapped
**Dawn Berwick**
I have PTSD

This is a photo of myself 4 years ago when I first started to use Art Therapy for my PTSD.

I added my first Art piece to my face which i gave the title 'TRAPPED' to express how I was feeling at that point in my life.

## Untitled
## Debbie Gardner

Pens on rocks

I have really struggled all my life to express my emotions in a healthy way until I found rock art and doodling. I started doodling on rock using colour and shapes to begin with and now realise I was actually starting a journey of self healing doing this. When I get overwhelmed it is one of the first things I turn to: Rocks and pens.

I like to hide some of them too and for myself this was another way of letting a certain feeling go.

Holding a rock keeps myself grounded too I have found.

## PTSD or Me
### Starr-Michelle Salvatore
I have PTSD


Vivid dreams,
They feel so real,
SO graphic, so painful,
Nightmares that won't go,
I can't tell the difference,
From living and not quite so,
What is reality I can't separate,
From the dream and the living,
Why do I feel this way? How long will this last?
Why is my head so fuzzy?
Why is my world spinning so fast?
I feel on edge,
I feel unhinged,
It's my trauma I know it's real,
But where do I even begin.
It's like I'm there,
reliving that day,
the moment my life,
Completely changed,
it won't go away,
it won't go away,
it's on repeat,
re-wind hit and play.

It's on my mind everyday,
I can't escape,
How much more can I take,
I don't want to dream
I don't want to feel
I don't want to experience it again,
But it feels so real,
I feel like I'm going insane,
I don't know of another person,
Who feels this way,
May be I am insane,

I am insane,
Maybe I'm not,
Maybe others feel the same,
Maybe I'm not alone after-all.
But why do I feel so singled out,
Why me I just want to scream and shout.
It's unfair I didn't ask for this!
Nobody asked I have to remind myself of this.
I'm not alone, I'm not alone,
There's so many struggling,
And So many have grown too
Take back control.
We want to be set free,
Set free from the condition,
That entraps us within,
We just want to finally be able to breathe.
We sometimes  wish we didn't dream.
We want to be able to tell ourselves
you're stronger than you know,
It's not me hun, I'm not to blame.. I'm doing okay.. breathe
it's not me, it's the PTSD.

I wrote this poem not to particularly share anywhere but to get what I was feeling in writing, to get all the words I wanted to say out. This poem has thoughts and feelings I often feel regarding PTSD nightmares. I wrote this at 3am after awaking from a vivid traumatic dream. The context is how I feel and I hope others can relate.

# Untitled
## Kirsty Bent
I have PTSD

Digital Artwork

I am a tattoo artist and my job helps me to heal others aswell as myself. The third eye represents being awake and seeing the world in a better perspective. She has believe written above her eyebrow as we have to keep believing in ourselves.

This piece is digital artwork and for me I find it therapeutic to create artwork. I do suffer with PTSD and have had quite a traumatic life.

Tattooing helps so much as it is a type of pain therapy. I love my job!

## Untitled
## Debra Purse

Sculpture

This is my mental health screaming during COVID. I have BPD and PTSD.

## Untitled
## Willow Hare

Felting

This is a felting of the Ring of Brodgar in Orkney.

Orkney is where I come to when I am having flashbacks - it helps me zone out... it's a different space for my head to go to.

## Untitled
Tanya Robertson

This piece signifies not giving up.

It was created from a series of paintings that didn't work, that were scraped off and ended up as the layers that created the foundations for something happier.

It symbolises flowers growing through mud, clawing their way to light and sun. It's unclear what is sky, what is water, which way is up and reflections are confused but this appears to add to the uniqueness and individuality of the piece.

Painting helps me to realise my own patience, resilience and uniqueness.

## Loose End
Jemma Furnival

I'm at a loose end today.
I can feel the edges ladder and fray,
Trying to plait myself back into the fabric,
But the fibres disintegrate away into madness.

## Untitled
**Grace Pashley**
I have PTSD

This is a painting I did after spending over a year in hospital suffering with PTSD.

When I got out at 16 I started an art course at college and painted this for an exam piece, to try and explain how I felt.

# Untitled

## Susan

In my head at night
I see this light
Things don't feel rite
My head is full of fear

Sleepless nites turn
into so much strain
my nightmares are
too much pain will
I ever make it threw
this dream again
I wish I could go
back start my.
Life all over again

Will I ever be the same
person again

One day I hope I see
the same light again

I never thought I would
be hear again my
Life was so much pain

but I know I'm going to
rise again Pain
       Trauma
       Sadness
       Dreams

This is my life how every nite I never thought I would ever see sunlight. My ex-partner hit me after that I didn't want to come out of this big black tunnel but my two boys were waiting on me to come out and see the light. They made me want live again x

**PTS'ssssssssD**
Shannon Workman
I have PTSD

Sketched initially with graphite pencils, coloured with charcoal pencils and soft pastel sticks and then defined with a ball point pen

Living with PTSD is complex, it's invisible and triggers often come in fast and strike at any moment, sometimes over and over.

PTSD can make you fear and avoid things or places you know to be a trigger, but it's not that easy, you can still (even years on) be surprised by random and unknown sounds or events, things that you wouldn't have any idea would be an issue until you are faced with them.

As inspiration for this piece (and to visualise how fast a trigger can strike), I just had the image of a snake as they are so so fast when striking, you fear them, but if you face them, handle them right and learn to overcome your inner fight, flight or freeze mode you can learn to manage them and even possibly use that strength to help others 'handle' their own triggers too.

# This is Now
## Nadia Henning

Just because it happened once
Doesn't mean it will happen again
Just because the world ended
Doesn't mean it can't begin.
It's okay,
Step away.
Hey, darling, you're safe.
You can stay.
Just remember that it passed,
And you know it will pass again.
Just remember it didn't last,
All the chaos and pain.
This is not the same.
You're in a different place.
Don't hide,   Don't crush it inside,
Darling, you're worth the tears you cry.
You were horrified.
No-one should deny.
But just because you lost your way,
Doesn't mean you're now unfound.
I know that you were sinking fast,
But this is solid ground.
You didn't drown,
Darling, you can swim and this is now.

This poem was written during a period of extremely difficult trauma treatment. Whenever trauma memories are at the front of my mind, I am unable to lie in the dark without having images of that trauma flash in front of me, so I sleep with the light on. I wrote this poem to try to give myself strength, and remind myself of why I was pushing through.

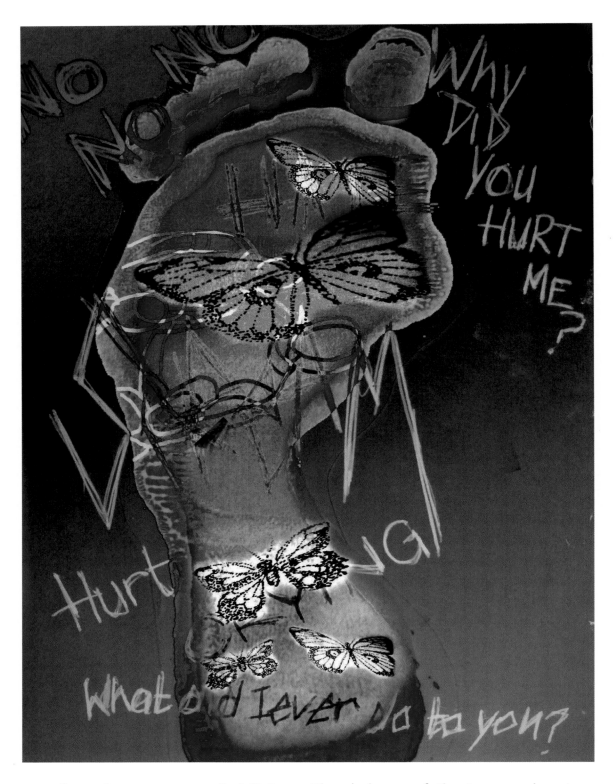

## Processing the trauma of child abuse
Laura Horsfield

Own Footprint as a child with scribbles from diary at the time scanned in to create a digital image

The darkness of the trauma changing your perception of the world
Remember it wasn't your fault
you can be anything you want to be
The colourful future is within you
Like a butterfly you will eventually be rid of the darkness and the Beauty will appear

## Leading Lines
### Jesse Cather-Long
I suffer from C-PTSD

Photography

Sometimes the road to recovery is a long and dark path. But if you look closely, there's light the entire way.

Taken in the Tate Britain.

For me photography is a way to show the world that some people see it differently, I love to show people how everything can be seen from different angles.

Photography is an escape from the world, and an escape from my mind.

## A lifetime ago
Ruth

Another lifetime ago,
I wondered where you had been my whole life.

Another lifetime ago,
I would see you in past memories, even though you wasn't there.

Another lifetime ago,
You made me laugh so hard and you made me cry so hard.

Another lifetime ago,
I saw the fight in your eyes, like a war that couldn't let go.

But now in this life,
I have to live the rest of my life without you.

Now in this life,
I have to learn to breathe without you.

In this life,
I have to learn to carry on without you.

In this life,
I also know what a gift it is to have known you.

In this life,
I feel truly blessed and grateful for the strength you have given me.

Yes in this life you still make me smile.
And in this life you still make me cry.

In loving memory of my best friend James who suffered with PTSD.

# This is Your Journal Speaking
## Wendy Fry
## I have PTSD

ALL your life
I mean ALL of it
Is welcome here
A place to share your hopes
Your dreams
Your fears
A haven to unburden yourself
To share your authentic voice
Perhaps for the first time
And not the last
Share with me your
Disappointments
Tell me of your heartbreak
Speak of your grief
Release your guilt
Reveal your shame
Unleash your anger
Express your pain
Those unspoken things
The events
Which you have never shared
Please tell me
I am here
Listening
Deeply
Be ALL of who you are
With me
Because you can
It's okay
I'm here for you
On those dark nights
Of your soul
I want to know
What keeps you awake at night
Share
ALL of it
I will listen deeply
Without judgement
I will support you

(continued overleaf)

Until your tears
And words are spent
Time and time again
You can visit me
You can stop by
When it suits you
We can share a cup of tea
I have your favourite biscuits in
Please know
I am here for you 24/7
When others fail you
Which is natural for humans
We can leave
Those people
To do their best
And we can
Get down to the business of writing
I will share with you
My truth
I want you to know
I, as your journal
I will not lead you astray
I will not disappoint you
I will not hurt you
I will not shout or tell you to be quiet
I can't promise
I will not make you cry
Tears are good
Let them flow
Little one
I'm here for you
I will listen
I will support
I will hold you
Gently
I will be Whoever or whatever you want me to be
As your journal
There is no limit to what I can
Do for you
Even when you let go of yourself
I am holding you
Know my words are true
I will be here for you

When you need me
Always
When you think
ALL is said and done
And you move on with your life
I will wait patiently for you
To begin again
Anew
Whenever you need me
I am here
For you
The time has come dear friend
To write from your heart
And share
ALL of who you are
With me

I created this art in the hope it will help others express their unique voice and overcome their personal traumas through journalling.

# Captive Set Free
## Sara Moon

I have been plagued with this anguish from such a long time ago, I am lost in the wilderness and its only pain that I know. There's broken dreams and fiery flames under me, I look up but its still only darkness I see, all I want is my freedom, I beg someone please find me. The chains are so heavy and I cant lift my head, so long I have lay here wishing to be dead. My jaw is clenched and my bones are aching, I can't stand up, I can't stop shaking. There's blood on my fingers from clawing so hard, there's ash all around me and my limbs are charred. There's smoke in my lungs and deep pain in my heart, what do you expect when I lost my counterpart. Now I'm left down here and there's no where to go, left alone with this haunting shadow. I submit to the darkness, there's no hope in sight, I can't see tomorrow, I'm giving up this fight.

Then suddenly I hear, like a knock at the door, He leans down and whispers that there is more. A giant, a guardian, the creator of life, scooped me from the fire and back into life. Restored and gasping after all this time, He takes my hand and says 'thou art mine'.

My piece is just a small snippet of my history with PTSD and C-PTSD and my journey back to light. I have been working with a therapist doing EMDR and it has really has been the only thing that has been able to shift the trauma for me. I have written lots more but haven't got the courage or confidence to share it but hope to do so in the future.

## Anger - Stop
Rebecca Clinton

Acrylics on a ½ inch thick piece of wood

In the depths of anger, I cannot do this anymore. I need help. Voices everywhere, people talking at me, telling me how it is, telling me I have no choice. I have to cope. But I cannot – LISTEN to me! They don't listen – STOP – leave me alone! I need to leave this world – I cannot do this ……. Taking charge, making a stand, I will not die this time, but now you are all listening…. I need Help!

Small piece painted in acrylics on a ½ inch thick piece of wood. No pre-planning – Using only my hands to manipulate the paint, I let my emotions lead the colours and movements that created this piece.

## Dissociation
## Nadia Henning

Pencil and pen

This is a drawing I did to depict how I felt during a dissociative episode the night before.

Abstract concepts can be hard to describe in words, so when I need to express something that I can't verbalise, I turn to artwork.

## Rocky Waters
Jesse Cather-Long
I suffer from C-PTSD

Photography

You may have had a rocky start, but beyond it there is beauty.

Trull Waterfall, Somerset.

For me photography is a way to show the world that some people see it differently, I love to show people how everything can be seen from different angles. Photography is an escape from the world, and an escape from my mind.

## So sick of this
Hannah
I have PTSD

Acrylic on heavy weight paper

I have PTSD as a result of my abusive marriage. As a result I have frequent flashbacks that trigger panic attacks that affect my life daily.

This piece is how I feel when I'm consumed by my PTSD. Completely absorbed by it and overwhelmed. I want to scream, shout, cry, hide and run away. It can be a very lonely experience.

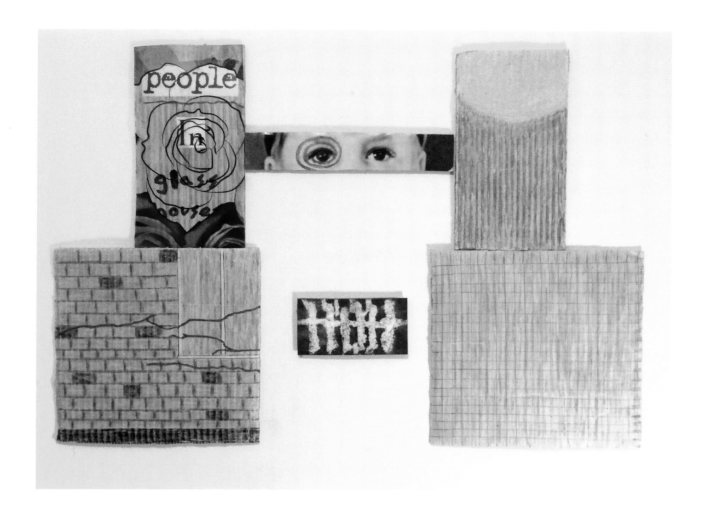

## People in Glass Houses
Samuel Humphrey
I have PTSD

This is a collage I drew/ made using cut-up cardboard from a single duvet set as the base. I was given the single duvet set when I moved into a Dry House February 2021.

I developed PTSD after a 3 month experience late 2019 to early 2020.

The experience, which I'm now receiving counselling for, deeply affected me and my ability to maintain sobriety and with the isolation of lockdown I had a particularly vicious relapse which is why I'm in a structured environment for 6 months.

The piece for me is about fragility. You will notice the crack in the structure of the house. This is related to the incident. I have turned to visual Art a lot since the incident.

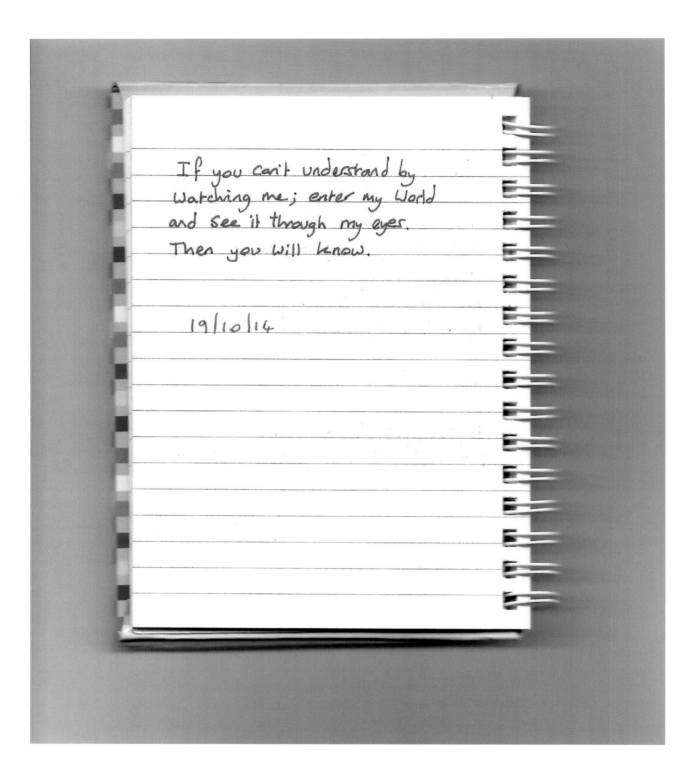

**Untitled**
**Kate Battye**
I have PTSD

This poem is about how people without mental health problems sometimes don't understand the struggles we who have these problems go through.

## Burden
### Darren Wall
I have PTSD

Here stands a man
A shadow of himself
Burdened by guilt
And failing health
Yet on the outside
You would fail to see
The trauma and pain
That resides within me
My apparent smile
Is perceived as joy
A simple disguise
I like to employ
My social disdain
Is seen in reflection
Yet...I masquerade
To avoid your attention
But as time passes by
The cracks, they appear
Leaking my soul
Through a solitary tear
Keeping a distance
Is the only way
To stop the trauma
Releasing today

This poem is very important to me as I have suffered with PTSD for over a decade. During this time I have struggled to convey how I am feeling to people that I know and love. I created my poems to help express those feelings, to try and give the reader a glimpse into my world, to help them understand my situation without having to explain my history or it's cause. Poetry is a cathartic release to me.

## Walk Alone
**Hattie**
I have C-PTSD

Acrylic paints

Producing this piece felt very emotional. She represents the bravery of continuing life after trauma and standing strong alone.

Using acrylics to make art really helps to ground me when I'm struggling with my C-PTSD.

# Sitting Alone
## Marie Cooke

Sitting here in this house all alone
Sometimes a prison this should be my home
No one ever visits I've pushed them away
I listen to others talking about how people stay
Sitting here alone night after night
Somehow I feel that this can't be right
But how can it change
When all think I'm strange
I don't go out, don't party or join in
Hate the nightlife and horrendous din
So instead I hide away behind these four walls
Sit waiting and waiting but no one ever calls

I wrote this to help me explain that even though I may have pushed people away and feel all alone, it wasn't intentional it was a coping mechanism when I couldn't explain to people why I would cancel plans last minute or go home early.

## Who am I?
Zoey Mc

I am the girl who hides away too often because her memories are too much,

I'm the girl who longs for adventure,

I'm the girl who often disliked herself, I'm the girl who has survived and will continue to...

I may struggle everyday but I will thrive!

## PTSD
### Carolyn
### My daughter has PTSD

How do you select who is your next prey? Reliving their terror day after day .
Weaving your evil spell deep in their brain, causing even more suffering and pain.
Their head full with emotions unknown, making them feel all alone.
Dragging them back into their own personal hell, moments they remember only too well.
Making them doubt their once clear sanity, for the sake of your own depravity.
Hiding away from day to day living, out of control, you are so unforgiving.
Struggling through as best as they can, evil atrocities witnessed by man .
Unable to keep your evil demons at bay, they lost their fight, their very last day.

My daughter was diagnosed with complex PTSD after a 7 month tour in Afghanistan, my poetry writing has helped me deal with her injury and also my own trauma while she was on tour.

## Remember her?
### Shannon Workman
I have PTSD

Sketched initially with graphite pencils, coloured with charcoal pencils and soft pastel sticks and then defined with a ball point pen

Having PTSD is a very complex condition and it can totally strip you of your identity.

Day to day you can struggle with so so many things and it often makes you feel that you have completely lost the person you were before.

I can remember standing there, staring at myself in the mirror and although I could see 'me' in the image that was reflected back, it was not the 'me' that I remember, or the 'me' I knew, it was more like it was a shadow version of me, just an empty shell, no spark, no zest, no colour to my being, and I wondered how the hell did I get here? Where has the fun loving me gone? and most importantly how do I get her back?

There is no fast solution, it's a long hard road to recovery (often littered with ups, downs and setbacks) but I know she's still in there somewhere and its worth the journey for that alone.

## For you, Mother
Lucy
I have C-PTSD

Acrylics on board

'The moor side still scares me,
Leaves me breathless and I wretch,
So on the moor side I set you free,
Feel my legs dangle from a ledge.

Flowers still bloom,
Cows are still to graze,
For death does not mean the end,
One day uplift will come of the haze.'

After losing my mother in difficult and scarring conditions I was left with a piece originally intended for her that I couldn't muster the courage to continue working on. I visited Langsett and other calming places to escape the torture of flashbacks and depressive episodes. I visited this place depicted time and time again after her passing. The escapism was a lifeline to me and so became this painting. Art has been my therapy and continues to be an outlet for the trauma I live with.

Though my mother was no longer around I needed to find positive relations with the world I was living in and continue to make art or at least finish the piece I had promised her. And so 'For you, Mother' was born.

## Storm in a Teacup
## Deborah Jane
## I have C-PTSD

Ceramic

The phrase "Storm in a Teacup" is usually used as an idiom to mean an over exaggerated response to something perceived by others as trivial or unimportant.

I started to use clay during the first phase of lockdown, as a therapeutic and playful way to take control of my own mental wellbeing; something I'd previously learned during my own personal counselling journey. Initially, to put words to my feelings and thoughts were extremely difficult, so visual aids played an important role as a way of communication. I was encouraged to keep a visual and poetry journal, which became the springboard for discussion during my counselling sessions. Storm in a Teacup - a ceramic piece, is of a girl in a teacup with a cloud hovering over her head and a paper boat balancing on the edge that represents, not only fragility and strength within an ever-changing environment, but the constant psychological and emotional hyperactive response state to a perceived storm brewing.

"Fate whispers to the warrior, 'You cannot withstand the storm.' The warrior whispers back, 'I am the storm.'" - unknown

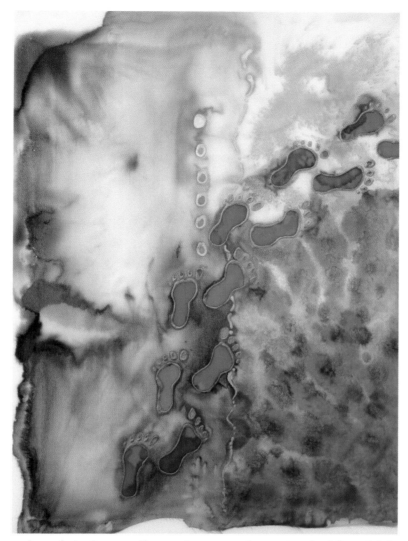

"We reach points in our lives where we have to decide which way we will choose to go. Do we keep on the same path, which is often easier, or do we choose a new way? It is often a frightening and difficult road to take, but ultimately we move from a place of hopelessness and despair to a place of hope. If we looked too far ahead we would be overwhelmed. Instead we need to just keep taking it one small step at a time and be gentle to ourselves along the way"

## Footprints for Change
### Rachel Nicholls
I have C-PTSD

Painting on silk

I started to paint images in silk which were inspired by my own journey through trying to recover from Complex PTSD and anorexia with the hope they may bring hope and encouragement to others who were also struggling.

## Inner Storm
### Amanda Carroll
I have C-PTSD

Acrylic paint, palette knives and my fingers

I was having a bad PTSD day. My emotions felt like a storm, my fear and terror where so strong, I was feeling overwhelmed. I quickly painted this with acrylic paint, palette knives and my fingers.

The big waves at the back mean for me the strongest waves of terror that could wash me away. A feeling of being tossed and turned with one flashback after another.

I find art for me is very good at calming down my overwhelming feelings, getting them down on paper seems to take some of the power out of my emotions.

## Tightening Gyre
Molly Kent
I have C-PTSD

Weaving

Tightening Gyre represents a new method of working for the artist, part of her new body of work 'Dream Weaving.' This work is the second completed weaving by the artist.

The work depicts an unidentified body, that of the artist, falling into the eye of a storm, through a tornado as lightning cracks around her. The work explores the feeling of falling without control, unable to right oneself in the correct direction, and feeling of turbulence within both mind and body.

## Vortex
**Christina D'Ascendis**
I have C-PTSD

Ink

This was drawn in ink at 4am when I was first struggling with effects of PTSD - a month of sleeping 2-3 hours a night and days of not sleeping at all. I drew this after I found out I would be having therapy. I felt release but also fear as I knew I would have to work through the trauma and I might get worse before I get better.

I felt naked, vulnerable and empty, but heavy at the same time. Art has helped me massively with symptoms as it gives me something to distract myself with and is a satisfying journey from start to finish. Art helps me express things that I cant find words to say.

# The Bergan.

## Ray Moxon

I have PTSD

This is my bergan of troubles.
This is my rucksack of woe.
The problem with this fxcking bergan.
Is, it goes wherever I go.

Some people say theirs is a monkey.
Others they have a black dog.
Well I have this fxcking great bergan.
It went along with the job.

It's packed with all kinds of memories.
Of some I never will tell.
To carry this fxcking bergan.
Isn't easy, in fact it's been hell.

It's never got any lighter.
Some people added more weight.
And carrying this fxcking bergan.
Is an effort I really do hate.

So. Rather than sitting complaining.
I know that I had to fight back.
To shoulder that fxcking great bergan.
Give in, not me? I'm no jack.

I have dug deep and faced the challenge.
Opened my legs on the climbs.
I'll get rid of this fxcking bergan.
I'll do it one step at a time.

So if like me you have a bergan.
A monkey or even a dog.
Shoulder the weight dear reader.
Push on even though it's a slog.

There IS light in the distance.
Push hard and you'll make it on through.
There's one person making the difference.
That one person really is you.

I'm ex emergency services as such my name is a Nom de Plume to keep my real identity confidential. I spent a lot of time looking for and dealing with people who had taken their own lives, as well as others. I was diagnosed with PTSD in 2018 and attempted suicide myself. I write poetry as a coping strategy. This is the first poem I wrote.

# Repeat
## Jemma Furnival

It's happening again.
My skin has turned to sweat.
Percussion in my chest.
Wish I could forget.

Smells stuck in my nose.
Fear lingers in the air.
I know this is the past,
But it feels like I'm there.

Was gonna go to bed,
But now I'm fucking wired!
PTSD release me -
I'm so fucking tired!

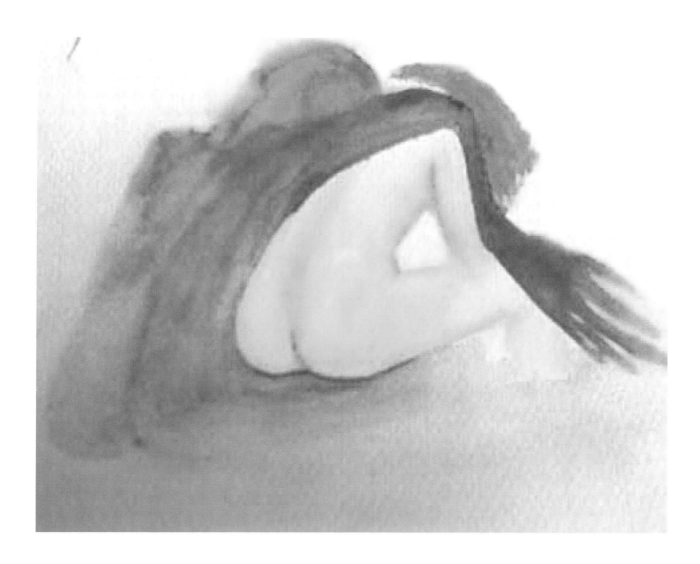

## Untitled
**Debbie Egan**
I have C-PTSD

I painted this before I got my diagnosis of Complex PTSD. I guess it speaks to the constant sense of fear and unhappiness that I carried around with me. Or since doing Internal Families Systems it suggests managers that were trying to keep me safe but suffocating me at the same time.

Painting has been a way for me to express the unspeakable..... it's often intuitive and I often have no idea what is going to come out.

# Writing
## Lauren Ruddock
I have C-PTSD

My passion was driven
By pain itself
Through trauma and sadness
Illness and adversity
Creative thoughts
Flourished through therapy and healing
Anger and emotion
Sadness and confusion
Poetry is the language
Of my wonderful mind
Words on the page
Calm my troubled mind
Pouring feelings from my brain to my keyboard
Fuel in my fire
Emotions are ink,
The pen is my sword
I write to move on
I write to feel less
Got me through pain and lots of upset
And mental illness
When the pen meets the page
I let go of distress, pent up rage
Anxious feelings and thoughts
Once they're written down
I'm able to reset.

Poetry has helped me a lot with my mental health, particularly my PTSD and depression. This poem was written in 2020, while I was undergoing EMDR treatment, which was successful, and this helped me to leave things, including the person who caused my trauma and related events, behind that I needed to help me to move forward, and I continue to write poetry as I enjoy both writing and performing it, and it helps me express emotions and thoughts that sometimes I don't feel that I can talk about but I can write about, and when I'm writing I can physically feel the weight of the emotions lifting from me.

# The Art of PTSD UK: The PTSD UK 'Rune'

The main structure of the PTSD UK logo is inspired by an ancient Viking symbol called 'Inguz'. The meaning behind Inguz is one of new beginnings – something we hope that PTSD UK can give to sufferers of PTSD and C-PTSD.

Inguz is also a rune of transitions and calls for us to leave the past and matters of previous situations behind us – it implies mental and emotional strength – the strength needed to achieve completion of a task, phase, or situation – and to move into a new cycle.

Simplified it means 'where there's a will, there's a way' and this has huge resonance with PTSD and C-PTSD, and the process of treatment and healing.

Our version of Inguz is actually comprised of 4 arrows, which signals the integration of the four 'selves': physical, emotional, mental and spiritual.

The arrows look back, forward, back and finally forward and therefore signal a drive toward completion, totality and a return to a life without PTSD or C-PTSD (whilst acknowledging that it's not necessarily a straight path through treatment to wellness).

The colours of the rune and our logo are comprised of colours of the lotus flower.

The lotus flower is a symbol of strength in adversity – they have the ability to rise from the mud, and bloom out of the darkness and radiate into the world. Just like you.

- Teal signifies courage
- Pink is hope
- Orange is success
- Purple is balance
- Grey is sincerity
- Lime green signifies confidence

We hope that we can inspire all these things in our supporters and those who need it.

# The Art of PTSD UK: Blue Sky and Clouds

You know the days where you just feel good. Your energy is high, you feel motivated and ready to take on the world. This is your blue sky. It may feel like it's been a while since you've seen it, but it's always there.

In the sky there are also clouds. Everyone has clouds: work stress, family stress, low motivation, money worries etc but the clouds that PTSD and C-PTSD can bring can feel VERY dark, VERY large and almost endless.

Sometimes a cloudy day is easy to manage, but sometimes the clouds build up and even feel like a storm is coming.

But what is important to remember is that clouds will always move. The blue sky is ALWAYS there, even if you can't see it at the moment. Behind every cloud is blue sky.

Tomorrow CAN be a New Day.

# What is Post Traumatic Stress Disorder?

Post Traumatic Stress Disorder (PTSD) is as ancient as humankind and can occur in all people, of any ethnicity, nationality, gender, occupation or culture and at any age.

It's a condition that some people develop after experiencing or witnessing a traumatic event or events.

It's estimated that 50% of people will experience trauma at some point in their lives. The defining characteristic of a traumatic event is its capacity to provoke fear, helplessness, or horror in response to the threat of injury or death Some examples of traumas include road traffic accident, being told you have a life-threatening illness, assault, childhood abuse, domestic abuse, burglary, witnessing a suicide or attempted suicide, natural disasters, traumatic childbirth, military combat, pregnancy loss, or admission to an Intensive Care Unit.

Traumatic events can make people feel that their lives are unpredictable, that they are out of control, that it's difficult to feel safe and trust others, themselves and their judgements of situations. Their experiences often feel unfair, unjust, inhumane and cruel and can make them question their assumptions about the world and other people. They can lose faith and easily become disconnected from others.

It's normal to have these emotions, along with upsetting memories, feeling on edge, or have difficulty sleeping after experiencing trauma - but eventually, the trauma or traumas fade to memories – painful, but not destructive.

However, around 20% of people who experience trauma go on to develop PTSD or C-PTSD. In the UK, that's around 6,665,000 people, yet it is still an incredibly misunderstood, often misdiagnosed and stigmatised condition.

# Why do PTSD & C-PTSD develop?

The human body is an incredible system, but it is also complex and full of feedback loops between body parts and brain. If you interfere with any of these loops dramatically (as in the case of experiencing trauma), you can affect the whole system.

If someone is exposed to an intensely fearful and traumatic situation, their body and mind 'suspend' normal operations and it copes as well as it can in order to survive. This might involve reactions such as 'freezing to the spot' or instead the opposite 'flight away' from the danger (it's been recognised that there are 5 main reactions to trauma – fight, flight, freeze, fawn and flop).

Your exposure to trauma can happen in one or more of these ways:

- You experienced the traumatic event
- You witnessed the traumatic event
- You learned someone close to you experienced or was threatened by the traumatic event
- You are repeatedly exposed to graphic details of traumatic events (for example, if you are a first responder to the scene of traumatic events)

Until the danger passes, many systems in the body are put on hold or adapted: your digestive system pauses, your muscles may tense up to be ready to flee or fight, your heart rate will increase, pupils dilate and the 'unimportant' task of memory creation is put on hold. This means that the mind does not produce a memory for this traumatic event in the 'normal' way.

Under 'normal' or non-traumatic circumstances, when information comes into our memory system (from sensory input such as what we can see, hear, taste, and smell), it needs to be changed into a form that the system can cope with, so that it can be stored. If the encoding doesn't take place due to a traumatic situation – the memory can't be processed. Instead, it is stored randomly, in pieces, in a variety of places within the brain.

Eventually, when the mind presents the 'memory' of the trauma for 'filing', or it is triggered by a smell, a place, or a person etc, it does not recognise it as a memory. As it understands, 'the brain is in the middle of the dangerous event - it is not 'outside' looking in at this event and therefore the entire system is not easily subject to rational control.' These flashbacks are incredibly distressing. Reliving the trauma as if it were happening RIGHT NOW. The elements such as the facts of what happened, the emotions associated with the trauma and the sensations like touch, taste, sound, vision, movement and smell are presented by the mind as real time information. They may also present as nightmares and intrusive unwanted memories.

These re-experiences and flashbacks are a result of the mind trying to file away the distressing memory and understandably can be very unpleasant and frightening because they repeatedly expose the sufferer to the original trauma. This danger response also sets off other stress reactions in the body such as blood pressure and heart rate increasing, blood sugar rising and digestion can be affected too. The body enters a state of hypervigilance so it is acutely (and sometimes inappropriately) aware of other 'dangers' around it, with increased startle responses.

In these cases, the body and mind are doing things they SHOULD do when presented with a threat. But humans are 'designed' for this to be an immediate fix, a short term solution which allows the body to settle once the threat has been resolved. But with PTSD and C-PTSD, it is almost perpetual. The trauma can physically injure the brain meaning it stays in the alert state for so long that it gets 'stuck' there and so begins to affect other systems of the body and mind.

The science and biology of this is quite clear and we know much more about how it affects your brain physically, but to summarise briefly:

- The amygdala in the brain is responsible for fear responses and fear conditioning. Exposure to trauma can activate the amygdala and related structures inappropriately, resulting in hypervigilance and 'improper' fear responses.
- The hypothalamic-pituitary-adrenal (HPA) axis is activated by trauma and the continual disruption that occurs with PTSD or C-PTSD is thought to produce damage in the hippocampus part of the brain which can show up as impaired memory.
- The part of the brain which regulates fear responses (the medial prefrontal cortex) is also impaired in people with PTSD and C-PTSD.

You can find out more about the regions of the brain that have been affected by PTSD and C-PTSD, on our website.

As the mind continues to try to repeatedly process the memory and the brain keeps re-triggering itself into 'danger' mode, people also find that their levels of awareness might change.

They can find it difficult to control their emotions and suffer intense symptoms of anxiety. This can present itself as both physical; shortness of breath, tight muscles, profuse sweating and a racing heart, as well as emotional: feeling on edge, hypervigilance (looking out for signs of danger all the time),

avoidance of reminders of the trauma or feeling panicky.

The brain is programmed to process memories and so the more the person avoids things like thinking about the trauma, the less likely is it that any memory processing will actually occur, and the more likely it is that further attempts at filing a memory will occur automatically. This ultimately leads to further nightmares, flashbacks and intrusive memories which lead on to further hyper-arousal and emotional numbing and this in turn leads on to more avoidance and so on. This is how the symptoms clusters perpetuate themselves in a vicious cycle which can go on for years – and when it goes untreated, PTSD and C-PTSD can last for decades.

"The injury is real. The injury is physical. It is not mere confusions or misdirected thinking, or sign of a weak character. It most certainly is not a case of 'Just get over it'". In some cases, symptoms can have a cumulative effect and can get worse rather than better over time, which is why some PTSD and C-PTSD sufferers 'manage' for such a long time without help, but they then worsen over time and eventually the symptoms become unmanageable.

For treatment to be successful, information and memory processing must be completed. This is why therapies such as EMDR aimed at helping the individual to process and work through the traumatic material are extremely beneficial. For some people, treatment can get rid of PTSD or C-PTSD altogether. For others, it can make symptoms less intense.

Treatment also gives you the tools to manage symptoms so they don't keep you from living your life.

# What is Complex Post Traumatic Stress Disorder?

While PTSD is usually caused by a single traumatic event, C-PTSD is usually caused by long-lasting, repeated or continuous trauma that continues or repeats for months, even years. PTSD and C-PTSD have very similar symptom 'profiles' and causes but C-PTSD also has 3 additional categories of symptoms (difficulties with emotional regulation, an impaired sense of self-worth and interpersonal problems) and can require more in-depth and time consuming treatment options to heal.

# Symptoms of PTSD & C-PTSD

PTSD and C-PTSD can cause a wide variety of physical, mental and emotional symptoms which can have a significant impact on your daily life:

- Re-experiencing is the most typical symptom of PTSD and C-PTSD. This is when a person involuntarily and vividly relives the traumatic event perhaps in the form of flashbacks or vivid nightmares.

- Avoiding situations, people or places that remind you of the trauma, or avoiding talking to anyone about your experience - this may make you change your routines and make you feel emotionally numb or cut off from the world

- You may be always on alert, jumpy and easily startled and on the lookout for danger. This may mean you have difficulty concentrating and sleeping (despite being exhausted) and you might suddenly become angry or irritable.

- Your emotions and the way you think about yourself and others may change. You may feel that nowhere is safe, that you can't trust anyone, have difficulty feeling positive emotions or feel guilt and blame about the trauma.

# Treatments for PTSD & C-PTSD

Just over a decade ago, people still thought that PTSD and C-PTSD were incurable conditions, but more recent evidence and research proves it is possible for PTSD and C-PTSD to be successfully treated many years after the traumatic event or events occurred, which means it is never too late to seek help.

- Eye Movement Desensitisation and Reprocessing (EMDR) is a powerful therapy which stops difficult memories causing so much distress by helping the brain to reprocess them properly.

- Cognitive behavioural therapy (CBT) is a form of therapy that aims to change the way you think and act in order to aid you in managing the negative effects through a broad range of different psychological techniques.

There are also other therapies and activities which can be used to ease PTSD and C-PTSD symptoms whilst you're waiting for these treatments, or to work alongside treatments, such as Art Therapy, running, swimming, EFT, Yoga, Martial arts, Acupuncture, Narrative Exposure Therapy, Writing and Journaling, Talking therapies, Hypnotherapy, Play Therapy for children and many more.

Some have short and some have long term effects, but when offered as part of a carefully formulated programme of therapy and coping techniques for PTSD or C-PTSD, they can offer people a welcome source of relief. You can find out about these and more on the PTSD UK website (PTSDuk.org).

# More about PTSD UK

PTSD UK was founded in 2015 by Jacqui after her own experiences suffering with PTSD. The lack of understanding, provisions and information made Jacqui realise that help and education is needed for those struggling with Post Traumatic Stress Disorder – along with their friends and family.

PTSD UK is the only charity in the UK dedicated to raising awareness of Post Traumatic Stress Disorder – no matter the trauma that caused it. We believe that supportive and reliable knowledge really is power when it comes to PTSD & C-PTSD. If you understand the types of trauma that can cause PTSD & C-PTSD, the physical, mental and emotional symptoms that are experienced and, most importantly, the treatments that can help you, then you'll be able to start down the path to recovery when you're ready.

We know first-hand that PTSD & C-PTSD can make you feel helpless, alone and isolated from those around you. So, we hope that knowing that someone understands a little more about it, is able to empathise with how you feel and will be patient with you, will help you feel more in control and ready to tackle it head on.

PTSD UK is here to provide resources and tools to inspire empowerment and resilience in everyone affected by PTSD & C-PTSD, to help them work towards recovery. We campaign to raise awareness of the condition, reach out to high-risk communities, help shape UK healthcare policies and give everyone the belief that 'Tomorrow CAN be a new day'.

Research shows that 10% of people will experience Post Traumatic Stress Disorder at some point in their lifetime – but it's estimated that up to 70% of people with PTSD & C-PTSD in the UK do not receive any professional help at all:

- Some people may realise they are struggling to cope after trauma, but are unaware they have PTSD or C-PTSD. They may feel that their symptoms are just part of their life now – even if they're debilitating and affecting every part of their life.
- For others who have a diagnosis, they may not know that treatments to help them recover are available. Just over a decade ago, people still thought that PTSD was an incurable condition, but more recent evidence and research proves it is possible for PTSD and C-PTSD to be successfully treated many years after the trauma occurred – but the treatment options for PTSD & C-PTSD are not as well-known as they need to be.
- Additionally, people with PTSD & C-PTSD are often misdiagnosed as they can develop additional disorders such as depression, substance abuse, problems of memory and cognition and other problems of physical and mental health. These 'co-morbid' conditions are what gets diagnosed and the PTSD & C-PTSD is left to get worse in many cases.
- For many people however, they're

simply unable to articulate how they feel, or feel able to reach out for help.

Our charity aims to raise awareness of PTSD & C-PTSD in three main areas – it's causes, symptoms and the treatments available. These 3 areas are of vital importance to those suffering with the condition.

- Causes: Many people have pre-conceived ideas of PTSD & C-PTSD, and what can cause it. There is a widespread misunderstanding that PTSD & C-PTSD only affects veterans, or those in the armed forces (likely due to it's previous name of shell-shock) but it can in fact affect anyone, of any age. It's vital that people are aware if they (or a friend or family member) have suffered a trauma, they should be mindful of trauma symptoms and the possibility of PTSD or C-PTSD.
- Symptoms: There are two areas in which knowing the symptoms are useful. The first is that people may recognise the symptoms in themselves (or a friend or family member) and reach out for help – starting their recovery process. The other is those who are suffering with PTSD or C-PTSD, can understand that what they're thinking or feeling, or how their body is reacting, is 'normal' for someone with these conditions – this can be of huge comfort knowing that once the PTSD or C-PTSD is resolved, those symptoms will be too. Some symptoms of PTSD and C-PTSD can feel totally unconnected to the original trauma or the condition itself, so it's really important people can recognise just

how PTSD can affect them.

- Treatments: PTSD and C-PTSD misunderstood conditions in many ways. Information about the treatments available is lacking and, at times incorrect. Just over a decade ago, people still thought that PTSD and C-PTSD were incurable conditions, but more recent evidence and research proves it is possible for PTSD and C-PTSD to be successfully treated many years after the traumatic event occurred, which means it is never too late to seek help.

In addition to those with PTSD or C-PTSD (and those around them), it's vital that healthcare professionals are aware of all of these elements to look out for in their patients to avoid misdiagnosis, incorrect treatments and to ensure their patients receive access to best resources.

# What does PTSD UK do?

### We raise awareness and are a voice for people with PTSD & C-PTSD

We produce and distribute supportive, reliable, high-quality and easy to understand resources, tools and information which are all backed by science and research. These help everyone (including Government, Medical professionals and the general public) understand the causes, symptoms and treatments available for PTSD and C-PTSD with the hope that people will be more understanding and informed, and know more about the daily reality of living with the conditions. We also work with the media (reviewing and informing scripts etc) to ensure accurate, non-stereotypical and informed portrayal of PTSD and C-PTSD in films, radio and television and have already collaborated with script writers from a variety of different productions including ITV, BBC and Warner Bros International.

## We provide resources to help empower those who need hope

We support and hope to empower people affected by PTSD and C-PTSD (along with their friends, family and carers) by providing knowledge, lived-experiences and resources to help them reach out for help, take control of their diagnosis, access the support and care they are entitled to, make informed choices, all to lead towards successful, sustained treatment and recovery for them or their loved one. Tomorrow CAN be a new day.

## We listen

Whether someone simply needs to offload their thoughts, direction on how to get help, or just know that they are not alone, we are here to provide resources and a warm welcome (even over email!) with compassion, experience and hope that Tomorrow CAN be a New Day.

## We improve services and support

We recognise (and have personally experienced) the gaps in the current service provisions for people with PTSD and C-PTSD in the UK, so we work with, and campaign to, the Government, organisations, policies and guidelines relating to the care and awareness of those with PTSD or C-PTSD, ensuring that we're all driving towards the same goal – that PTSD and C-PTSD is recognised, diagnosed and effectively treated as quickly as possible for everyone.

## We research

We promote, undertake and collate research that can answer vital questions about PTSD and how people affected can be supported and how treatments and care can be evaluated, improved and be made more accessible.

## We share the knowledge

Our resources are used by a variety of health professionals, organisations and other charities – we want the knowledge about PTSD and C-PTSD to be as far reaching as possible so we always offer interviews and case studies to media outlets, research papers and projects where possible. Our information and resources are referenced by a variety of organisations and publications including The Economist, BBC, ITV, The Independent, Women's Health, CNN, Huffington Post, The Metro, The Week and The Big Issue.

We don't expect people just to find us – sometimes, we need to go to them. We reach out and establish links with high-risk communities across the UK such as the Emergency Services, Rape Crisis Centres and Victim Support Services along with other charities which support people who are at risk of PTSD or C-PTSD such as parents of children with disabilities.

# PTSD UK's vision

Our vision is to transform the lives of people affected by PTSD or C-PTSD, supporting them to take control of their diagnosis, access stigma-free support and resources and work towards successful, sustained treatment and recovery.

# PTSD UK's mission

Our mission is to provide supportive, reliable, high-quality and easy-to-understand resources to educate, help empower and inspire resilience in everyone affected by PTSD or C-PTSD, to help them work towards successful, sustained recovery. We campaign to raise awareness of the condition, reach out to high-risk communities, help shape UK healthcare policies and give everyone the belief that 'Tomorrow CAN be a new day'.

# How can I support PTSD UK?

If you are looking to get involved to support or fundraise for PTSD UK – THANK YOU!!

We are the only charity in the UK dedicated to raising awareness of PTSD, so your donations or support, big or small, let us do work that is truly life-changing for people affected by PTSD and C-PTSD. Thank you.

You can find out more on our website about events, our online Supporters Store, fundraising challenges and other ways to help support PTSD UK - PTSDuk.org

# MY OWN THOUGHTS & SCRIBBLES

_____
_____
_____
_____
_____
_____
_____
_____
_____
_____
_____
_____
_____
_____
_____
_____
_____
_____
_____
_____
_____
_____

# MY OWN THOUGHTS & SCRIBBLES

# MY OWN THOUGHTS & SCRIBBLES

_____

_____

_____

_____

_____

_____

_____

_____

_____

_____

_____

_____

_____

_____

_____

_____

_____

_____

_____

_____

_____

_____

_____

_____

# MY OWN THOUGHTS & SCRIBBLES

_____

_____

_____

_____

_____

_____

_____

_____

_____

_____

_____

_____

_____

_____

# MY OWN THOUGHTS & SCRIBBLES

_____

_____

_____

_____

_____

_____

_____

_____

_____

_____

_____

_____

_____

# MY OWN THOUGHTS & SCRIBBLES

_____

_____

_____

_____

_____

_____

_____

_____

_____

_____

_____

_____

_____